M000236683

THE INGRID PITT

BEDSIDE COMPANION FOR

GHOSTHUNTERS

FOREWORD BY
Uri Geller

B T BATSFORD · LONDON

© Ingrid Pitt 1999

Drawings © Jim Bailey 1999

All rights reserved. No part of this publication may be reproduced in any
form or by any means, without permission from the Publisher.

Printed in Great Britain by Butler & Tanner Ltd, Frome and London

For the Publishers
B.T. Batsford
9 Blenheim Court
London N7 9NT

ISBN 0 7134 8444 6

A catalogue record for this book is available from the British Library

CONTENTS

FOREWORD

by Uri Geller

"ALL HE WANTED was for the hideous screaming to stop …" "Deftly she stepped to one side and hit him in the face with the bloodied carcass …" "Slowly, as the packing case tilted and tipped over to crush the trapped man, he heard the sound of the boy's laughter rise and swell until it filled the universe …"

There is only one woman who can chill the soul with such lush, theatrical gestures. Everything about her is magnified and distorted by a cracked camera lens – the Eye of Horror. When she wishes us to observe, she does not point – she extends an imperious finger, its nail sharpened to a rapier tip. When she wishes us to listen, she does not speak – she cascades words with sweeps of her gore-dipped quill. When she wishes to terrify, she piles up our nightmares and, with lashes of her whip, drives them over the brink into the Pitt.

She is the Countess Dracula. She is the Witch-Queen of the Screen. When she quietly asked if I would provide a few words for her new book, I recognised the request for what it truly was – an imperial demand that I could refuse at my direst peril. These pages are full of foolhardy mortals who thought the power of their reason was stronger than the supernatural. I am not that stupid. Or perhaps, after reading this volume at a single enthralling sitting, I am simply scared out of my wits.

Take the Countess's book and place it by your bedside.

You may never sleep again…

Uri Geller

The Grey Lady

A lonely figure, breathless in the night
Fading, silently, softly out of sight
Re-appearing so tantalising and bewildering in the mind
Gliding gracefully, this ghostly apparition needs no place to hide
The air is still; no time to breathe
Your heart lurches and your chest begins to heave
Like a touch of earth upon your skin
The sudden cold makes you shudder within
You question your thoughts about the 'Grey Lady' being true
But her presence is known only to the Chosen Few.

Caroline Purser

1

Introduction: The Grand Canyon

Flat Tyre on the Oldsmobile

To bring the dead to life
Is no great magic.
Few are wholly dead:
Blow on a dead man's embers
And a live flame will start.

Robert Graves *To Bring the Dead to Life*

I WAS LIVING in America. My marriage had just disappeared down the plughole, the theatre company I had been working for had folded its tents in the night leaving me and my beautiful daughter, Steffanie, with a clapped-out Oldsmobile, virtually destitute. When this sort of disaster strikes the only thing you can do is pass it down the line. The stiff upper labia revolves around cosseting your resources and to hell with everybody else. I followed the example of the departed stock theatre company, placed the carrycot on the passenger seat, the case with my gear in the trunk, let off the brake and freewheeled down the obligingly sloping drive from the boarding house to the road, kicked in the motor and headed out of town. It didn't matter where, exactly, as long as it was over the State-line and my irate landlady might find it difficult to set the police on me. I was really in a bind. The little money I had I needed for baby food. Luckily petrol was amazingly cheap at that time so I was able to put some

mileage under the threadbare tyres before they finally gave up what I must call the ghost if I am going to get a pun in this early.

A stroke of luck. I had the blow-out on a road that passed an Indian Reservation. Native Americans hadn't figured much in my life up until then. Like everybody else I had a guilty feeling that they hadn't been getting their fair share but, when you feel that your share seems to be even less, I can't say you care a lot. Just off the road was a corrugated iron shack with car hubs nailed all over it. I hadn't seen that sort of decoration before. They reminded me of the memorial shields you sometimes see in stately homes displayed along the beams. A youngish lad was stretched out at the side of the shed on a pile of tyres. As I approached, he opened an eye and watched me suspiciously. He brightened up considerably when he noticed the flat tyre on the Oldsmobile. He tried to sell me one of the tyres he had been sleeping on but when I asked him to fit it for me he admitted that it didn't fit. He must have seen how upset I was because he came over all solicitous and promised he would get me a tyre. He knew where there was one that was practically brand new and I could have it for a quarter of its true value. I didn't believe him but what other options did I have? He asked me to look after the store and disappeared. I sat on a tyre and let the misery hang out. An hour passed, two hours. I had just decided to push on with the flat tyre when a skinny little girl in a frock two or three sizes too big came shyly along the dust path and stopped a little way off. She just stood there saying nothing. I smiled and tried to look friendly. She didn't respond. I had Steffanie on my lap so I turned her so that the little girl could see her. Little girls are always suckers for babies. Not this one! Babies meant hard work as far as she was concerned. I'd had enough. "What do you want?" I snapped. She looked as if she was about to run off but I quickly switched on a smile and she calmed down. "You're to come with me," she said quickly. "Whoa," I thought. "Not so fast." I'd heard about tourists who broke down and were never seen again. On the other hand what had I to lose? I had no money, a broken-down jalopy and a hunger that was mounting by the second.

I was expected. As I walked into the little collection of clapboard and corrugated iron shacks I could see dark, melancholy faces peering out at me. There was still the fear that I was about to become a statistic on a police blotter but I didn't care. Around the back of what turned out to be the general store was a pile of junked cars. An old man limped out to see me and cuffed the girl around the ear as tactile confirmation that she had done a good job. She didn't hang about but sped off towards the store. The man introduced himself as Johnny Running Bear and told me the girl was his granddaughter Rose. By this time I was weaving in and out of reality. I hadn't had a proper meal for a week and that day had only eaten a packet of crisps and an apple I had picked off one of Johnny Appleseed's

trees by the side of the road. Everyone seems to be called Johnny in the mid-west. Johnny or Elmer. I slumped against the side of a rusted wreck and tried to explain my predicament. He wasn't listening. He walked back towards his shack and called his woman. I found out later that was what he always called her. Her real name was Indian and translated as "Woman who walks forward." She came out reluctantly. She was shortish with a wide flat face, very indigenous, and long, well-brushed, grey speckled hair. She took one look at me and hurried forward. She supported me and urged me towards her tiny house. Inside it was dark and furnished with seats and bits and pieces from scrapped cars. It was cool and I gratefully sank into a back seat salvaged from a Dodge. Woman fetched a scrupulously clean aluminium bucket of water and I gratefully washed the sweat and dust from my face. When I was refreshed she offered me food. I protested weakly. I didn't mean it and tucked into the dish of beans and potatoes she put in front of me while young Rose fed a bottle of formula to Steffanie.

The upshot of it was that I stayed with Johnny and his family for a couple of months. I found them generous and kind but desperately unhappy. As much as I began to hate the authorities that had condemned them to a life on the poverty line in such a wealthy country as the United States of America, I had to admit to myself that much of their problems they brought on themselves. Instead of looking around and accepting what they had got and building on it they sunk their troubles at the bottom of a whisky jar and consigned their future to fate ... and to whatever smart Alec lawyers might be able to wrest from the US Government as restitution for the loss of tribal lands. I shot off a couple of letters to Jack Kennedy explaining what he should do. I obviously embarrassed him because he never wrote back.

One of the side lines that Johnny had was taking tourists down into the Grand Canyon. A couple of times a month he went and collected a dozen or so horses and a well-off

cousin arrived with a mini-bus-load of would-be wranglers kitted out self-consciously in cowboy duds. Johnny allocated the horses and they set off down the long winding trail to the floor of the canyon. I desperately wanted to go but I was already sponging off his family and simply didn't have the nerve to suggest that he put off a paying customer and took me instead.

Inevitably the time came when a would-be cowboy didn't turn up. Johnny generously offered me the horse and I suddenly had doubts. Horses and me had never really got on. I would have liked to be able to smile sweetly and demur. That's my problem. I always know the right thing to do but almost inevitably choose the opposite.

We left at dawn, Johnny leading the way and one of his sons playing tail-end-Charlie. I was just behind Johnny with Steffi in a basketwork frame attached to my chest. I was terrified. Not just for myself but for poor Steffi. What would happen if the horse tripped and fell or went berserk and plunged over the side of the canyon into the river far below? Gradually my confidence began to build as the sure-footed animal eased effortlessly downward.

It was afternoon when, without incident, we got to the prepared camp site by the side of the Colorado river. The other tourists thought that I was part of the management. I didn't disillusion them. If they thought that I was a blonde, blue-eyed Iroquois why should I spoil their fun? That night we all sat around a roaring log fire and felt like hardy homesteaders. Unlike the homesteaders we had the comfort of knowing that our Indians were friendly. As the fire died down I got drowsy and cuddled Steffi closer to my body and stared into the glowing heart of the fire. Gradually the rising sparks and shifting logs began to form a face. A face I had loved and lost. My rational brain tried to tell me that I was building castles in the fire. My emotional brain didn't want to know. The face that had

formed in the golden embers was the face of my father. I also had the overwhelming feeling that he wanted to see my baby. Without hesitation I pulled the poncho I had wrapped her in aside so that her face was exposed and held her up so that he could see her. Tears cascaded down my burning cheeks. I swear he smiled and nodded before shifting logs destroyed the image and it flew, in a trail of sparks, up towards the moon now peeping over the side of the canyon.

I'll never forget that experience and even now, if I'm feeling a little depressed, I think of that golden moment in the Grand Canyon with my baby and my father.

Well that's my credentials for writing this book held up for scrutiny and probably found wanting. Found wanting because it is very difficult to describe exactly what a ghost is. In films the ghosts seen to be generally benign. The gruff but loving captain in *The Ghost and Mrs Muir*. The affable Topper and the follow-ups. Robert Donat's puzzled Scottish laird, shipped to America with the stones of his castle in *The Ghost goes West*. Not so benign are the ghosts of *Hamlet* and *Macbeth*. There does appear to be a virtual cottage industry of houses with malignant natures and transport, in the shape of planes, carriages and ships, seems to get more than its fair share of infestation. All of these manifestations differ. Some ghosts are interactive. Others just hang around ineffectually watching their successor making the same sort of bloomers that they made in life. Usually the ghost manages, in some obscure way, to make contact with their beloved. Always toward the end of the film and always to get the living hero out of a hole. Need we look any further than *Ghost* with hunky Patrick Swayzse trying to get on earthly terms with the copiously weeping but magnificent Demi Moore and finally making the breakthrough with the aid of hilarious quasi-medium – Whoopi Goldberg?

2
So What is a Ghost?

If there are ghosts to raise,
What shall I call,
Out of hell's murky haze,
Heaven's blue hall?

Thomas Lovell Beddoes *Dream Pedlary*

GHOSTS HAVE BEEN with us since we dropped out of the trees and took our chances against the quadrupeds inhabiting the undergrowth. As one would expect, the Greeks and Romans did a very nice line in spectres returning to plague the living. The Greeks' qualification for ghostship required that the person dying to give birth to his other dimensional self had to be killed or die in an abnormal way. Passing gently away in the arms of the family didn't qualify. It was also believed that the spirits only slept and it was as well to pass through the cemetery very quietly or risk awakening them. The Romans wanted their departed spirits more amenable. The average ghost could be very helpful to career or love-life if approached properly and respectfully. Even so you had to be careful. If the departed spirit had departed from someone innately evil then the ghost could be something to be avoided.

China and India had plenty of roving spirits, most of them with a fixation about delivering as much misery and misfortune as they could to those still in a corporeal state. They also spent a lot of their haunting time in the guise of an animal: any animal as long as it could scowl and look reasonably ferocious. The problem is that they seem to get mixed up with other forms of fright-life like demons, vampires, ghouls, incubi and generally mayhem-inclined devils with horns, tails and fiery breath. Not exactly the ghosts I had in mind.

My sort of ghost has the same basic qualifications as a genuine, down-to-Hades vampire. It's got to be dead. And it's got to haunt something or someone. Benign or malign doesn't matter. After all – it is possible that they are both different aspects of the same living person. It also has to be visible or at least have some marked effect on its surroundings. Shy, banging, groaning, plate-throwing, smell-projecting entities just don't do it for me unless they can at least come up with a shadowy outline. When someone claims that they "know" there is a presence in the room because the temperature drops I'm not interested. Rising hairs on the back of the neck do nothing for me. Solid objects falling off the mantelpiece is interesting but not, of itself, a ghostly manifestation.

The islanders off the shores of Australia believe that the departed spirit, departed from the body that is, has a touch of the old Chinese Yin and Yang about it – Yin being "aunga" or good, Yang, the "adaro", the evil side of man's nature. After death ghosts go to live at the bottom of the sea or in a volcano. Some even make the journey to the moon. "Why" is the question that goes unasked. Ancient Egyptians also had some finely rooted ideas about what happens after death. They saw a sort of extension of the present form and made sure they were not mistaken for a *fellah* of the field by taking along whatever expensive goodies they enjoyed in life. This included food, animals, chariots, golden death masks and the odd handmaid or two. Ancient Egyptian ghosts obviously find their new circumstances so much to their taste that they don't bother to return unless they happen to find themselves in a ghostlike form. Then they come back as either a deity, a pharaoh or a scarab beetle pushing a dung-ball across the sky. Like syphilis, ghosts know no boundaries and are to be found in every culture. Some, like the American Indians, believe that the spirit lives on forever and takes up residence in the trees, grass, wind or animals when it quits the earthly body.

The Christian religion, in many ways, makes the whole thing easy. When someone dies the spirit shuffles off into a state of limbo where it can ask all the questions it couldn't get an answer to when in the solid state. Like why didn't I win the lottery? Or why did Jayne Mansfield have bigger breasts than me? When all the answers are given and the value of the soul judged it is either consigned to hell or Heaven. Hell is just one long orgy in an overheated room with overloud heavy metal music. Hanging around on fluffy clouds trying to master the fingering on a harp and not lusting after angels and other assorted forms in see-through negligees is what you get if you're handed a ticket to Heaven. Which means you get three shots at the ghostly manifestation business. One is the wandering around looking sad and lonely bag which results from the uncertainty of hanging around in limbo waiting for the call. Heavenly ghosts seem to have a penchant for appearing in sleazy sitting rooms in Blackpool, claiming to be an Indian Chief guide and telling the gullible – who have coughed up £10 each for a chance to hear something to their advantage – exactly what they want to know.

Most of the really good hauntings come from the third group who have been consigned to hell so, unless someone in the uncommitted world does something pretty magnanimous to right the wrong done by the unhappy spirit, the poor lost soul will not be allowed to pass upwards. Again I would like to quote *Ghosts* as a perfect case in point. When Patrick Swaysze dies defending the delicate Demi Moore he is in limbo, waiting for the outcome of his appeal that his sell-by date has been unjustly brought forward. When he is finally happy that everything has been done to make Demi completely unhappy and unfit for any further relationship in the real world, he is called to the other side in a blaze of joy. Not so the nasty "friend" who turns out to be the author of all Swaysze's misery, Tom Goldwyn. He is dragged away to the fires of hell by a bunch of evil midgets in black habits with blazing eyes.

The Christian church may deplore the vehicle but the plot just about touches base on all the relevant points. There is a divergence between the ghost of the dead of the Protestant church and their rivals for the Holy Ghost's favour, the Holy Roman Catholic Church. Basically the Protestants don't believe that ghosts are after-life representatives of the dead, but evil spirits pretending that they are. Catholics generally accept that ghosts once lived a sentient, full-blooded life and do return in their altered form to pester the living – but only to ask for their prayers or to right an injustice.

Spiritualists – on the third spectral hand – believe that ghosts are graphics of souls that are earthbound because they have slipped through the system and don't realise they are dead. That's why they are eager to talk to any old biddy with a terrible hairdo, an

aspidistra and a tom-cat that insists on marking its territory daily.

Dickens' ghosts in *A Christmas Carol* were ghosts of a different ilk. These represented events – except poor old Jacob Marley, of course. He not only had to rush around in December with nothing but his winding sheets to keep him from disintegration but he had to drag the miseries of his life, the accounts and records ledgers, around on a great clanking chain.

Marley, like many other ghosts, was liberated from the brickwork by the night. Generally speaking ghost-lovers prefer to have the object of their disquiet rattle their chains at the witching hour. But it ain't necessarily so. Versailles is a case in point. Nearly a hundred years ago two middle-aged ladies coughed up a couple of francs to have a vicarious thrill walking through the gardens and halls that hosted the best and worst of pre-Revolution French monarchs. They turned a corner and got more than their money's worth.

Strolling around on the lawn and through the ornamental gardens were scores of highly rouged men and women in eighteenth-century dress. As the ladies went out of the palace gates they mentioned to the man on the turnstile that they enjoyed the pageant put on for their benefit and were gobsmacked when he told them they were talking through their *chapeaux*. That stroll through the Versailles gardens in 1901 made the two English schoolteachers, Eleanor Jourdain and her friend Ann Moberly, famous. A year later Miss Jourdain returned and claimed to see a gardener who wasn't there as well as not seeing a couple of labourers loading a cart – all in broad daylight. Since then, several other visitors to the palace have claimed to have had similar ghostly encounters but, as they had already been exposed to the writing by and about Mesdames Jourdain and Moberly, it doesn't count. That's my kind of ghost. Fancy-dressed, mobile and interactive. But there are all sorts.

3
Berkeley Square

I was not there, you were not there, only our phantasms.

T S Eliot *The Family Reunion*

LONG BEFORE LOVE-LORN Hooray Henrys mooned around claiming to have heard a nightingale singing, Berkeley Square was already famous for more sinister and less melodic sounds in the night. Number 50 not only had a ghoulish Victorian-style landlord, hand-wringing, ear-piercingly abused, innocent young girls and self-impaling sailors but, in addition, gave off a charge of static electricity that could knock your wig off – allegedly.

Now the house is indistinguishable from others around it. But a hundred years ago it was a mouldering ruin with little to recommend it but a clear view of the newly installed urinals in the Square. Its descent from a decent pied-à-terre for the hopefully upwardly mobile to a clapped-out derelict began in the middle of the nineteenth century when a Mr Myers was in residence. It could well be that, in fact, Mr Myers was the prototype for the fanciful lover out-warbling the mythical nightingale of Berkeley Square. Crossed in love by a young harpy who was no better than she should be, the sensitive Mr Myers retired into the back bedroom, roaming the house at night in a tatty nightgown by the light of a single candle and having intercourse, commercial as far as the story goes, with the son of the local general provisioner who supplied all his needs.

As the spurned suitor grew older and more malevolent

and the house took on the superficial decorations of the dismal Frankenstein castle, its reputation for evil and supernatural visitations grew. It was claimed that the walls themselves became hostile to the outside world and that an incautiously placed hand could result in hair like a boxing entrepreneur and teeth fizzing out of the gums like popcorn on a hot griddle.

Out on the town for a weekend of trying to drink as many taverns dry as the King's shilling could afford, a couple of sailors from the *HMS Penelope* ended up in Berkeley Square in what can only be described as a state of advanced rat-arsedness. By this time the moody Mr Myers had been called to whatever paradise blighted lovers are called and the house had become more of a wreck than during his neglectful stewardship. But the mist from the burns of Scotland had fogged up the eyes of the two jolly tars and, looking for a cheap place to rest themselves in preparation for the next days jollities, they kicked in the rotting front door, stumbled up the stairs and crashed out in the first place they could find that boasted some glass in the window and shelter from the chilly night air.

What happened after that can only be speculated upon. Zonked out on some rotting drapery, a whole foremast to the wind, it couldn't have been very easy to awaken them. Something did. Something so mind-boggling that pink elephants dancing across the ceiling and rainbow-hued snakes squirming out of the walls paled to insignificance. In terror the two seamen rushed around like a second-rate cast on a Keystone Kops film before the more agile of the able-seaman saw the only way out – the faint outline of the undraped window illuminated by the guttering gas-lamps in the square below. The, by now, not so jolly tar, saw the light as his salvation and dived headlong through the glass. Like the old adage commands, he should have looked before he leaped. Before the Second World War demanded that all metal surplus to requirements should be turned into artillery and bombs to blast the evil Jerries, every self-respecting house sported a fine display of iron fencing. This was usually in the form of Roman spears, standing on end and braced by a connecting strut. As our leaping able-seaman soon found out when he ignored the adage and plummeted down at 32 feet per second. His anguished cries as he hung from the steel shafts embedded in his rectum, à la Edward II, were only slightly less pitiful than his shipmate's, whose mind had been completely short-circuited by whatever he had seen and who was huddled in a corner making disgusting un-animal noises.

Even in those days, Berkeley Square was inhabited by the gambling set. Gambling really meant gambling then. None of that nipping down to Hill's for a flutter on the 3.30 at Ascot. Wagers were made *mano a mano* on practically anything: water running down a window pane, who has a hole in his sock or, visions of *Les Liaisons Dangereuse*, who could bed the latest virgin on the block in the shortest time.

The reputation of 50 Berkeley Square had grown so rapidly that it was a major topic of conversation at the *soirées* and salons that made life bearable for the chattering classes. At first the hard men and gamesters ignored the tittle-tattle: they didn't believe in the supernatural. You had to put your faith in real, solid,

charms like a well-mounted rabbit's foot or a hair from the tail of a horse that had won a race and been struck by lightning and survived. Very efficacious – the latter.

Still the stories of odd goings-on at Number 50 persisted – and were embellished. The story of a pretty maid taken into service by a lascivious employer and kept locked up in an attic room was a big favourite. It was posited that it was the unquiet shade of this poor, distressed creature that had so terrified the sailors on leave that one had ended up spiked and the other screamed out his eternity in Bedlam. It was a tale that fed the public imagination and, before long, there was a whole bunch of quivering psychics ready to swear to having seen the pale tortured face at the upstairs window, pleading to be delivered from the unnatural advances of her lecherous master. The Victorians were big on lecherous landlords and simpering virgins. The gaming classes also had an interest in virgins – simpering or plain – as long as they were willing.

Then a Mr Bentley, either an extremely foolhardy bloke or an out-of-towner who hadn't heard the tales that were freely circulating, took on the lease. He moved in with his household and set about bringing the house back to something approaching its former semi-grandeur. Not an easy task. It wasn't just that the house was decrepit. There was also the smell. It wasn't just that every dosser and blade with a bladderful had used it as a stand-by urinal for a couple of decades. It wasn't that every pigeon from Waterloo to Trafalgar Square had unloaded in the unglazed rooms. Or that rats had proliferated, died and rotted in the variety of excreta and dust that had dominated the rooms for years.

There was another, unearthly smell. The smell of Satan's Inferno was the generally accepted opinion. Mr Bentley, an investment made, wasn't to be put off by the objections of his nasally sensitive family and declared the refurbished house ready for occupation – and hired a maid. The maid, Alice Warmsley from Walthamstow, was not what you might call romantic. She had spent the first 14 years of her life working in her uncles' tanning pit and had a skin that had absorbed more than a little of whatever it is they rub into untreated skins. Being taken on as a skivvy was a major breakthrough for the Warmsley family and Alice was determined to return to Walthamstow a lady – well, at least a lady's maid.

To Alice the house smelled like a dawn walk in the Vienna woods after the tanning sheds of her childhood and she settled into the garret without a problem. Bentley was grateful for this. Now if his daughters continued to complain he could point to the maid's easy acceptance of what was positively the worst room in the house and make sneering remarks about their fragile understanding of the world about them.

For a while it almost seemed that his hearty insistence that nothing was wrong was going to work. Then one of his daughters brought her boyfriend home for a weekend of family fun. The only room where the gallant captain could fit in, other than the daughter's – and Bentley wasn't having any of that – was the room that had proved so ruinous to the sailor boys and frequently displayed the ill-used maid at the window. Bentley offered his daughter's suitor the fatal room but first warned him of its reputation. The young soldier, aware that the room was only a short distance from that occupied by the frisky object of his lust, smiled deprecatingly and claimed that he would sleep in no other room.

A striking example of loins speaking before the brain is in gear!

Alice was dispatched to make the room ready. The family was downstairs taking tea and listening to the tales of derring-do that the captain was embroidering for them when the bone china came to the edge of disaster as a blood-chilling scream echoed through the house. Those in the parlour sat *en tableau* for seconds before

Mrs Bentley gave a fair imitation of the primal scream, daintily replaced the Daltonware on the sidetable and swooned. Bentley was of sterner stuff and leapt to his feet. "Come with me!" he ordered his martial guest and ran from the room. The captain, who would have preferred to stay and bring solace and comfort to the ladies, reluctantly followed.

They found Alice standing in the middle of the bedroom, a newly ironed sheet crumpled between her hands, staring wide eyed in the direction of the window. Bentley spoke sharply to her but she didn't react. She stood, rigid as a day-old corpse, her mind locked in some place not accessible to the others. Nothing they could do could bring her out of her trance so the benevolent Bentley had her stowed safely away in her garret and gave his guest the opportunity to forget the idea of staying over and return to the safety of his barracks. It was no good. The captain's lust made him impervious to any argument that the older man might put up.

So the household retired to bed.

The captain gave himself a good scrub down with carbolic soap and waited for the wee small hours when his beloved's resistance would be at its lowest ebb. The tryst was not to be. The family were awakened by the sound of a pistol shot. When they managed to break into the guest room they found the captain dead – his face a mask of horror. From the attic came the sound of insane laughter. Alice was packed off to a hospital the next day and died, insane and uncommunicative, a short while after. The captain's death was put down to a brainstorm.

All this excitement added to the house's reputation and, from being a subject for idle conversation, became a source of interest to the gambling classes. Here was a readymade set-up that could only gain by notoriety. The dare was set. A thousand guineas for anyone who could spend a night alone in the house. First up, and last, for what looked like easy money, was Sir John Warbouys.

Known as a committed drinker, esoteric gambler and a self-acclaimed lady's man, he accepted the rules of the challenge. He must enter the room before midnight, must be completely alone and could only carry a small side-arm. As a concession he was allowed a bell. This he could give a playful tinkle on the hour to show he was still up for the game and, if he needed assistance, he would ring the bell as frantically as the conditions dictated. The Knight sank a large port and brandy, said goodnight to his adjudicators who were to spend the night outside in the garden, and retired.

An hour later came the first all-clear signal. By this time the witnesses were wishing they were somewhere warm and comfortable and trying to think up an excuse to slide off to a well-frequented establishment on the other side of the square. For the second time the bell rung out and the gamblers grunted their disgust and settled down deeper into their blankets and coats. They never heard the bell again. Whether this was because they all went to sleep or because it never rang again is open to dispute. Naturally the witnesses refused to admit that they had nodded off, but if they weren't asleep why didn't they remark on the fact that the bell didn't ring. Hadn't they read Conan Doyle?

When, finally, they decided to look in on Sir John, they found him in exactly the same condition that Mr Bentley had found the captain. Dead with his features hideously distorted.

What manner of apparition could cause the death of hardbitten men just by its appearance? Was there something about the house's history back beyond the broken hearted Mr Myers that could account for the reign of terror that had invaded the house?

Well, there was the multi-talented parliamentarian, George Canning who, when he wasn't sorting out difficulties in South America, lived in Number 50. Perhaps he was up to something untoward. Maybe he ran

a concession from the recently disenfranchised Hellfire Club in the attic. Or brought back some devilish voodoo practices from South America. Probably not. When he died in 1827 the house was bought by Miss Curzon of the famous Curzon family who owned big tracts of land in that area. She died in the house at the grand old age of 90 and never complained of anything untoward. So maybe she was the malignant spirit?

Again unlikely.

Mr Myers, who bought the house from her executors and, after being dumped by his fiancée, spent the rest of his life wandering around the house in his nightshirt lit only by a farthing candle, was never known to comment upon any supernatural activity.

Let's be uncharitable and pile it all on to Myers. Maybe his heartache extended beyond the grave and he wanted everybody to know about it and suffer. And maybe the reason that the present occupants – the antiquarian booksellers, the Meggs Brothers – have reported no death-dealing apparitions is that Mr Myers, firmly ensconced in the theoretical hereafter, has either won over his lost love or found someone else to supplant her in his affection?

*

In 1933 Jesse Lasky, the man who made Hollywood, produced a film written by John Balderston, the ex-journalist responsible for rewriting the *Dracula* stage play of Hamilton Dean's London success and making it into an American blockbuster, called *Berkeley Square*. The plot is about a house, surprisingly, in Berkeley Square, that takes pity on its owner, who isn't getting a fair deal by the local female populace and catapults him 200 years into the past when, evidently, time travellers had a far better time of it amatorially. Leslie Howard played the lead in his usual frail manner and Heather

Angel matched his delicacy as the girl from long ago. Matching the general limp-wristedness of the film was the directing of Frank Lloyd. It was all very languorous and the script couldn't miss the opportunity of inserting a few cunning *déjà vus* into the fabric of the past.

The events in *Berkeley Square*, the movie, in no way echoed the fatal confrontations in Number 50 but it is interesting that the writer should pick Berkeley Square as a setting for the whiplash into the past. The book from which Balderston wrote the screenplay was by Henry James, *A Sense of the Past*. It's more than a little likely that James had heard the tales told of Number 50 Berkeley Square and decided to give the disquieted spirit of Mr Myers a solution to his problem. A trip to the past and a lady who would indulge his habit of wandering around in his nightshirt.

Whatever the basis for the story, it was considered good enough to get a further outing in 1951 with the more robust Tyrone Power taking over the Howard role. Christopher Reeves, then the incumbent Superman, decided the story was the sort of delicate métier he needed to prove his worth as an actor away from the supernormal exigencies of his man-of-steel character and reprised it as *Somewhere in Time*. Another location switch and the 6ft 4in Reeves trying to look and act like the effete Leslie Howard. Not a pretty sight. Jane Seymour, the love interest, is at her most beautiful but somehow never manages to make the time-lock.

And, of course, that was the end of any connection with the haunted house in the heart of Mayfair.

4
Ghostly Gazumping

Thou canst not say I did it: never shake
Thy gory locks at me.

William Shakespeare *Macbeth*

IF THIS IS LONG ISLAND it's got to be Amityville. Which means 112 Ocean Avenue. And we all know what that means. The little seaside resort of Amityville was in the wallow between Trick or Treat and the hypocrisy of Thanksgiving. Usually a time when nothing more exciting happens than deciding whether the Halloween costumes can be put away for use again next year and trying to think up an excuse for not inviting the new neighbours around for turkey and toasted marshmallows. Except at Number 112 that is. Ronald De Feo, one of the sons of the household, found his bank balance wasn't keeping pace with his spending habits. So he took a gun and ventilated the rest of the family, his parents, two sisters and two brothers, where they sat. His rather unoriginal plan was to blame some unknown marauder, wait until the resulting hue and cry ran itself out and then slope off to spend the quarter of a million dollars his father had thoughtfully insured the family for. Having done the dreadful deed Ronald worked himself up into a Stanislavskian sweat and dashed into the nearest bar and sobbed, cried and screamed as he told the tale of how his family had been slaughtered. Unfortunately for Ronald the local police chief was a simple man who worked on a simple premise. In a case of murder you first suspect the hysterical witness who has witnessed the slaughter but has miraculously survived. Ronald fitted part one. Next was

who benefitted most from the crime. Ronald was up for that one as well. Fingerprints on the gun, bloody footprints in the hall and witnesses to the actual trigger-pulling weren't as reliable as the old and tried theories so the Sheriff arrested Ronald De Feo and he was subsequently handed down six life sentences to run consecutively.

In the year that the old house stood empty it picked up a bit of a reputation. Strange lights, unearthly shrieks and a good deal of grunting and groaning was heard at night but this was put down to the manifestations of the hot-blooded younger generation. As long as the teenage pregnancy rate didn't rise too steeply, no one felt called upon to do anything about it. Anyway, a new family had already slapped down a deposit and were threatening to move in immediately.

The new family were the Lutz, Kathy and George and their offspring – a five-year-old daughter, Missy, and two sons, Danny and Chris. This was 1975. The year Saigon fell and Karpov got a walkover in the chess championship when Fisher failed to show. A year of little excitement unless you happened to be on the spot. And it seems that the Lutz family were on the spot. George was up to his hairpiece in alimony and his construction business was on a downward slide. He might not have been so pushed if it wasn't for his wife's insistence that it was time for them to move up in the world. Deer Park might sound nice but it was in a low-rate area and didn't impress their social climbing friends. When George heard the asking price, he couldn't believe it. It was a bit more than he was paying at the time but the push to his upward mobility would more than compensate for the extra money he would have to find. At least that was the general thinking which dominated the build up but was out of the window almost before they installed their obligatory rubber plant in the living room. But it was too late to bow out gracefully. There was work needing urgent attention. The drains had silted up and rain had seeped in during the year that the house had been uninhabited and plumbers and brickies don't work for nothing. George decided he would have to do the work himself. He had the skill but was woefully short on motivation by this time.

At first his guileless remarks to neighbours about black gunge flooding up through the drains and dark patches appearing on the walls were merely stated facts. His audience, generally speaking, had a more colourful imagination. Before long the gunge was congealed blood and the dark patches bloodstains. These solid manifestations were linked with the shrieking, moaning and general background noise heard when the house was unoccupied, and a legend was born. George, to be fair, just went along with his neighbours to begin with. It gave him an excuse for not being more eager to bring the condition of his dilapidated house on a par with his neighbours. The more the stories circulated the wilder they became. Before long George and Kate had forgotten what was real and what had been invented for, and with, the neighbours. Once the idea that the home was actively working against him had taken root everything that happened took on a sinister aspect. At least it distracted him from the unpalatable fact that he was heading for a nasty appointment with the bankruptcy court. The expense of keeping up with the Rockefellers was prohibitive. But at least he had an excuse. Now there wasn't just the slime in the bathroom and the blood on the wall to contend with – the slime became a stinking morass and the

stain actually exuded glutinous globules of blood. This attracted millions of flies and the smell became unbearable. Then the symptoms of supernatural possession became physical. Kathy was in the bathroom about to step into the bath when she felt strong arms encircle her. Her husband was out and it was the gardener's day off so she let off a shriek and fought her way out of the bathroom. The proof that the arms were at least unusual were the livid weals that covered Kathy's body. George was sympathetic but he had his own tale to tell. He had woken up in the night to hear the martial sounds of a band. A marching band. The crashing cadenzas of the music and the tramp of marching feet shook the timber-framed house to its foundations. Again it was Kathy's turn to feel the force of whatever was spooking the house. They had both just dropped off to sleep when she was jolted awake by a falling sensation. Her scream jerked George awake and he stared open mouthed. Kathy was hovering several feet above the bed bathed in an unnatural glow. Before George could move the light snapped on and one of the children, woken by the ruckus, appeared in the door. The interruption short-circuited whatever force was levitating Kathy and she crashed back onto the bed.

Things started to hot up after this. Now the place was besieged by huge hooded figures that walked through walls and appeared at inconvenient moments – although only when the family were alone. The hooded ones were joined by a grotesque demon with only half a face. The other half looked as if it had been blown away by a shotgun. Evidence of an earlier haunting that had not worked out too well for the ghoulish figures?

By this time George had become unhinged. What with his business worries and keeping the family funny business alive he had jumped the final cog. He was now convinced that he was a reincarnation – if you can be a reincarnation of somebody still alive – of the murderous Ronald De Feo. Never a day passed without his reporting some new and unexplainable occurence. One night, for no apparent reason, the family were jolted out of their sleep by a tremendous crash from below. When George went to investigate he found the heavy, solidly fashioned front door ripped from its hinges and lying in the hall. On further investigation the following morning he found that the garage door had been vandalized to such an extent that it needed replacing.

And then there were footprints! Not any old footprints – cloven-hoof prints in the snow. You might think that any normal household would have packed what was to hand in the nearest duffel bag and been long gone by now. Maybe it was George's newly acquired persona as the De Feo doppelganger that kept him at the centre of things. Whatever it was, he was still willing to face it out.

Until the night of the fiery eyes. These were seen by the six-year old daughter. They seemed to float outside the kitchen window glaring malignantly at those within. That was enough for Kathy. George she could cope with. Levitation had its lighter side and, hey, what's a phantom cuddler between sharing entities. But fiery eyes outside the kitchen window was too much. By the morning the family was long gone - and the mortgage company could whistle for its money!

Naturally by this time the Amityville Horror had hit the press. Each time it was strained through a different reporter the story was reinvented and embellished. De Feo's lawyer saw the mounting histrionics over the supernatural inhabitants of the house as a basis for an appeal. Ronald De Feo had always maintained that voices had implanted in him the undeniable urge to slaughter his family. His lawyer now tried to convince a judge that the demonstrably malignant nature of the house was the basis of any argument for a retrial. The press loved the story. It was all hearsay and malarkey but when straight-laced lawyers tried to convince sceptical judges that it was all true, they had a field day.

When Jay Anson finally decided to write the book in 1978 the Amityville Horror was so well known that it was hard to find an angle that hadn't been exploited. So, using the minimum of poetic licence, Jay got together with George and wrote the story. Before the book was off to press the story had been snapped up by the film company INT/Americana.

Although the whole affair might seem just a little OTT the overwhelming success of first the book and then the screenplay stirred up the main contributors to the story, the witness De Feo, the lawyer William Weber, "Father Mancuso," the exorcist, Jay Anson and the whole of the Society for Psychical Research. Soon everybody was suing or threatening to sue every one else.

At the box office the film was going from success to mega-business. James Brolin and Margot Kidder headed up the cast as the stressed-out George and the over-wrought Kathy. Rod Steiger came in and, just in case anyone was in any doubt that the story was in any way fruity, played the priest as if he was giving acting classes to a bunch of walkabout deaf Aborigines who had knocked off his toupee. The music, by Lalo Schiffrin, did get an Oscar nomination and the film was acclaimed by the box-office tills.

Not willing to let a good thing slide silently under the table the Amityville Horror was quickly followed by exploitation movies of ascending direness and an unbelievably bad TV series.

The capper is that the new owners who took over the house sued George Lutz, and won on the grounds that their peaceful existence in the house was disturbed, not by entities from beyond the great divide but by tourists who couldn't get enough of the place. George Lutz and Jay Anson, together with the producer, had to cough up over $1,000,000. Even the lawyer Weber had a go at the much misused Lutzes claiming that the whole shebang had been a put-up job between George and Anson with the idea of writing the book the prime objective. Can the path of literary endeavours ever have been so fraught?

5
Spectral Guidance System

...ghosts are fellows whom you can't keep out

T.S. Eliot *A Fable for Feasters*

PUT ERROL FLYNN in a snug pair of tights, comb in a bouncy page-boy hair-do and top it with a cute little green hat with a long feather and what have you got? A hearty, butch Robin Hood. Immaculate dinner jacket, quizzical eyebrows, a fastidious need to be shaken and not stirred and a penchant for killing off his second lead ladies gives you an exciting James Bond. Even diddy Dudley Moore, navel high to the statuesque Bo Derek and getting a ten for ambition is still within the parameters demanded of a sexy lead character in an overbudgeted film.

But Richard Dreyfuss!

It takes a bit of imagination on the part of the audience to squeeze chubby little Dickie, with his perpetually petulant expression, into the heroic mould. It's what they call casting against character. In the film *Always* it is definitely that. Dreyfuss is cast as a devil-may-care pilot. Not just any old pilot but a gung-ho fire-fighting pilot. His job is to bomb forest fires with foam extinguisher. This calls for real low-level stuff, snapping off the top branches of blazing trees whenever the camera is in the right position. Love of his life – and subsequently his death – is feisty little Holly Hunter, also a pilot but more often the voice on the radio reminding our heroes what their job is. Inevitably Dreyfuss goes a bush fire too far and dies trying to return to base. Luckily for the film,

although dead, he refuses to do the decent thing and go to the pilot's heaven. Holly Hunter wanders around for a while with a sorrowful face and a glycerine tear or two before falling for the masterful charms of replacement pilot John Goodman. All this is observed at close quarters by the defunct Dreyfuss. Understandably he is a bit miffed to see his bereaved girlfriend heading towards connubial bliss after only ten minutes' sprocket time and tries to influence her into giving the presumptuous toerag the big E. But another forest is out of control and another squad of gallant fire fighters is trapped in the encircling flames. The new boyfriend wants to show his prowess but Holly Hunter has been there before. Anyway, women's lib dictates that somewhere in the picture Holly has to turn off the waterworks and take control. So while everyone else is discussing the best way to put out the fire she sneaks off and takes the plane up into the wide blue yonder. Sitting in the co-pilot seat – but of course unknown by Holly – is concerned Richard Dreyfuss.

To save the trapped men below she is forced to fly impossibly low. She does the business but the plane has been fatally damaged and Holly is feeling pretty groggy. It looks like Dreyfuss has got what he has been hanging around for. If Holly dies he can stick a couple of spectral fingers up to his replacement and be reunited on the astral plane with his paramour. Of course he doesn't. The plane behaves impeccably while he wrestles with his conscience. A decision made the aeroplane goes back to behaving badly and Dreyfuss with the half-conscious aid of Holly, manhandles the controls and regains the airfield and safety. Waiting there is her new lover who wraps her in his arms right in front of the ghost of Dreyfuss. Fortunately Dreyfuss has now realised that hanging around the airfield isn't going to make eternity any shorter so he wanders off into the sunset.

Always is a remake of *A Guy Named Joe* with Spencer Tracey and Irene Dunne but suffers in comparison. The flying scenes and towering flames overshadowed the cast and in spite of the Oscars in the cupboard and the charismatic aeroplane the film hasn't got a lot to recommend it. Except, maybe, the idea that sitting in the co-pilot's seat when there's a state of emergency on board, is a know-it-all spirit who can fly the stricken plane to safety. A comforting thought half-way across the Atlantic when the pilot unexpectedly asks you to fasten your safety belt. Unless you go a thought too far and ask how the ghost-pilot got into the spectral fraternity. There does seem to be some sort of provenance for the story. One of the best concerns sibling RAF pilots. Links between identical twins are said to be pretty common. Why shouldn't they be: there's the same blood and mould and life expectancy. In brothers of a different age a mental tie-in is not so common, unless there is a focal point that can knock down the barrier of age. Bill and Jim Corfield had flying. Like all heroes of the forties Jim wore a uniform and set his younger brother's eyes shining with hero-worship when he came home on leave and relived his moments of glory on bombing raids to the Ruhr. Billy wanted some of that. He was an avid reader of *The Champion* and never missed a chapter of Rockfist Rogan, RAF. Jimmy was Rogan - and more. Another year and Billy would be

old enough to join his brother and together, he had no doubt, they would put an end to Nazi aggression. Jimmy wasn't too keen on his younger brother getting his wings. He felt responsible for his enthusiasm. The stories Jimmy told were lurid and ultimately upbeat but that was just for non-combatant consumption. He was aware that few bomber aircrews thought much beyond their next breakfast and the majority were disappointed even in that. Unfortunately the more Jimmy tried to discourage his kid brother the keener he got. In a desperate effort to head him off Jimmy extolled the virtues of ground crew. Billy was not to be sidetracked. He still had Rockfist Rogan as guide and mentor.

After the Battle of Britain the war turned against the Axis powers and thrusting raids into the heart of occupied Europe became a daily routine. Routine but deadly. On his eighteenth birthday Jimmy led 44 Blenheim bombers on a low-level raid on Cologne. It was a daylight raid that was supposed to catch the German fighter pilots by surprise. Daylight raids were usually the forte of the American airforce but in August 1941 they still hadn't got their act together. The slow-moving Blenheims dodged the ack-ack and withstood the first attack of the fighters sent up to intercept them. As the defenders regrouped above them the Blenheims unleashed their load and turned for England and hot buttered toast. Like crazed hornets the Messerschmitts dived to the attack. With no aerial defence but their on-board armoury the Blenheims could do nothing but empty their barrels at anything that came into the gunners' sights and count the smoke trails as one by one the lumbering bombers crashed to earth. Twelve planes dived in before the coast and a welcoming squadron of Spitfires rescued them. It was too late for Jimmy Corfield. The first in on the bombing run, he had borne the brunt of the massed Nazi fighters as he struggled to gain height.

The death of his adored brother made Billy even more determined to become a pilot. He would have preferred to be a fighter pilot but the demand was for bomber pilots and he had to take that or find something else to do to win the war. By the time Billy was authorised to wear his wings the war was over bar the treaty signing. A couple of years flying Wellingtons and Lancasters and a stint in Transport Command on Dakotas qualified him for a post-war career as a civilian pilot. This was before flying became subject to lots of paper qualifications. It was still possible to get your hours in and fly the civilian routes purely on experience in the air.

One of Billy's first long-haul flights was to Singapore. It meant a series of shortish stages and a good deal of dead-reckoning navigation but, with a co-pilot and navigator on board, there was no reason to think there would be any problems. Even the weather was being helpful. The forecast for the Athens leg of the trip was CAV.OK. Clear skies and happy landings. Then, unpredictable but predictably, the weather closed in. Not just a little gentle precipitation or some scattered woolly clouds – real, down to sea level fog topped by some high-level turbulence. Without the use of electronic aids, flying in a white-out on grade one eyeballs was a distinctly hazardous business. For a while they pressed on hoping they would run into the wonderful flying conditions they had been promised before they took off. Some hope. The upper air turbulence followed diving atmospheric pressure and, before he knew what had happened, Billy was fighting to keep the plane airborne. Desperate to find out exactly where he was he nosed down through the grey cloud in an effort to see what was below. He prayed there was nothing high and hard. At 50 feet he caught a glimpse of the sea and levelled out. The crew heaved a sigh of relief. They found the Ionian Islands but in the circumstances that was a blessing not too well disguised. There was no time to relax. The navigator punched Billy on the shoulder and pointed to the left. Through the swirling sea mist he caught sight of a rocky coastline. While the pilot cautiously edged his way towards the coast the navigator made a guestimate of their position – somewhere in the north-eastern Mediterranean was the best he could come up with. But a navigator needs to be resourceful as well as optimistic. As they flew parallel to the breaking surf the navigator saw a break in the cliffs. Without hesitation he told Billy to turn left – into the jaws of the Corinth Canal. Billy didn't hesitate. For the last 15 minutes he had been trying to convince himself that the time had come to put the plane into the sea and call for the Mae Wests. Any hole in a cliff was better than that.

As the wings came level Billy wondered if ditching hadn't been the better option. The cut where the Canal went through the cliffs looked impossibly narrow. Committed – he gave up a small prayer. And the buffeting wind seemed to stop on the instant. There was a new spirit in the cockpit and Billy knew that the spirit was brother Jimmy. He felt the tension flood from him. Inside the walls of the Canal the air was impossibly tranquil. The plane bisected the canyon smoothly and without any of the customary buffeting associated with flying in close proximity to the ground. The more Billy relaxed the easier it got. Jimmy flew down that dark canal more surely than any guidance system ever invented could manage. For nearly five miles Billy left the flying to his dead brother. He knew, absolutely, that with Jimmy in control, there was no danger.

The end of the Canal was reached without incident but still the weather was zonked in and there was nothing to guide them to a safe landing. And now they were really in trouble. It's one thing to be waltzing around the skies with a full fuel load and an expectation of better weather before the needle on the fuel gauge hits the stop. It's a different tin of pilchards when there's nil visibility and

the needle on the fuel gauge is already bouncing off the stop. Before Billy could become too morose considering the deadly alternatives he felt Jimmy take over and gently turn the plane a few degrees to starboard. Billy let it happen. There was more certainty in the move than in either the navigator's guess of where they were or in his own gut feeling that they were going to be alright.

As suddenly as he had got the feeling that his long dead brother was with him, guiding him, the sensation went. One moment Billy was sitting in the left hand seat, a passenger, comfortable in the knowledge that he was being looked after by a higher power, the next he was fighting to control the aircraft in the treacherous crosswind. He felt like crying out for Jimmy to come back but he didn't have time. Right in front of him the lights of Athens airport had, almost miraculously, appeared. With the engines spluttering and banging on the last fumes of their fuel load the plane sank onto the runway. As the wheels hit the tarmac one of the engines cut, followed by the second before they had time to taxi off the runway.

Of course nobody believed their story. Fly along the Corinth Canal – impossible. Wing-tip clearance was practically nil and the wind gusting between 30 and 40 knots would have slammed the plane into the walls before it even got into the cut.

For a time Billy protested that his story was true but after a while learned to live with it and make a deprecating crack about "ghost-flying" if anyone reminded him of his hair-raising trip along the dark canal. In his heart he knew that it had been his hero, his brother, who had returned when he was in peril and brought him safely to harbour.

The Corinth Canal flight is not the only instance of ghostly presences aboard aircraft. There is hardly an airfield in Britain that doesn't boast a spectral aircraft or a ghostly pilot. Some scenarios are quite complex.

Aircraft sighted getting ready for take-off and the pilot interacting with a witness. Aeroplanes that appear on the glide path in the gloaming and cause confusion to a pilot about to land. There is even a pilot decked out in helmet, Mae West and flying boots who was known to turn up in the WAAF dormitories to the consternation of all.

As more aircraft take to the skies the venues for airborne apparitions increase. But, for me, the ghosts of Spitfires, Hurricanes and Battle of Britain pilots take a lot of beating.

One of the most unusual turned up in 1988 at a little airfield in North Yorkshire called Hinton-on-Ouse. Although it was regularly used during the war it had sunk into insignificance once the machine guns had been turned into bicycle frames and the "pukkah gen" dialogue had given way to more mumbled phrases. Unlike most airfields, which could field a ghostly dog or a shadowy pilot if pressed, nothing had been seen in or on the RAF station that could not be put down to overindulgence at the NAAFI or the Sergeants' or Officers' Mess.

W.O. Hodgson had a pretty crappy war and his return to civvy life hadn't been exactly a bundle of laughs. Most of the war had been spent in a POW camp after his plane had been shot down on a bombing raid. He had been one of the escapees featured in the Steve McQueen movie *The Great Escape*. After the war he never seemed to get his act together and died in 1959.

Nearly 30 years later it was decided that it was time to honour his memory by putting a plaque up outside the control tower. The ceremony went without a hitch but the plaque had hardly weathered in when a decision was made to bring it inside. This move may or may not be the cause of what happened next.

It had been a pretty boring shift for assistant traffic controller Brenda Jackson. No air traffic meant she had been left on her own while her superiors – at least her seniors – slouched off to reminisce in the bar. A movement attracted her attention and she glanced up from the latest Air Notes to see a pilot, dressed in World War II battle gear gliding along outside her window. Brenda didn't have to consult the notes to know that this was not standard RAF practice, so she let out an uncontrolled high frequency alarm to notify anyone in earshot that she was not happy. By the time the officer of the watch had swigged back his port and lemon, buckled his belt and found his hat the figure had disappeared. Brenda wasn't thanked for her early warning of an alien invader. In fact it was generally accepted that she had nodded off and wish-fulfilment had delivered up the romantic image of a Brylcreem fly-boy.

Then he appeared again!

This time Brenda wasn't alone. The controller Flight Lieutenant Brine was with her. Brenda saw the apparition first and repeated her high decibelled "View hello." Brine turned as white as any ghost and only just managed to control his sphincter before the ghost gave

them a mournful last look and vanished. Now that it was official that the control tower was haunted it wasn't easy to get anyone to work there late at night by themselves, so an official inquiry was launched. Debriefing Brine and Brenda Jackson gave them enough to work on and it was soon decided that the haunting was being orchestrated by W.O. Hodgson – he of the recently installed memorial plaque. As the hauntings had only started after the plaque was moved inside the general opinion was that for some reason he didn't like confined spaces. After all, his dying instructions were that he should be cremated and his ashes consigned to the care of the westerly wind on Runway 22.

The answer was obvious: move the plaque back to its original site. That was the end of any supernatural hanky-panky at RAF Hinton-on-Ouse but on a dark night when the wind is in the west and the moon and the hazard lights are vying for dominance, there is an uncomfortable feeling that somebody – or thing – could be trying to sneak into the darkened control tower.

6
Around the Bend

The extravagant and erring spirit hies
To his confine

William Shakespeare *Hamlet*

RACING DRIVERS, in spite of their job, are usually pretty boring people, focused utterly on their machinery and the next time they are going to jump the starting flag and beat their fellow competitors into the first corner. When they aren't discussing gear ratios, going through Lesmo flat or who the girl with the big headlamps and aerodynamic chassis is they seem to congregate in photographers' studios dressed in the latest racewear and practising a sneer. Not at all the type you would suspect of having a tie-in with a supernatural being. A world champion – Mike Hawthorn – no less.

But that's what Peter Gammon confessed to a motor-racing journalist, Dave Nye. Gammon claimed that he was in a race at Brands Hatch in Kent in the early fifties when his contact with the other world happened. At that time Brands was little more than a narrow strip of poorly preserved tarmac with an area on the side of a hill that was laughingly called The Paddock, a tin-hut that doled out tea and wads and not an armco barrier in sight. Nobody even knew what a safety belt was and crash helmets were for sissies. The theory was that if you went off the track the mud would slow you down. If you were unlucky and hit an inconveniently sited tree you would hopefully be jettisoned from the car into the soft, yielding, aforementioned mud.

If not – well – the race tracks of those days were a fruitful culling ground for the Grim Reaper.

Peter's first encounter with the hereafter was at Druid's Hairpin, a slow corner at the top of a short rise. The idea is to steam up the hill, hit the brakes hard, change down to second or first, power around the corner, hopefully avoiding the other cars, straighten up the car and ram home the power on the downhill section to Bottom Bend. The secret is straightening up the car before ramming the foot down on the hot pedal. Peter didn't get it right and was seriously out of shape with 30 cars coming blind out of the corner and bearing down on him. Before Peter Gammon's bacon could be cooked the car miraculously straightened out and he plunged on through Bottom Bend and went on to complete the race.

Now comes the dodgy bit. Peter went to a spiritualist meeting. For some reason the medium homed in on him and told him that someone called Mike, who had recently gone over, was trying to contact him. Peter owned up to knowing Mike Hawthorn. Brilliantly the medium deduced that Peter was a driver and had recently had a near accident. A bit like saying you are an ice-skater and nearly fell over recently. Through the medium Mike also apologised for hurting Peter when he took control of his car and applied his enormous skill to get him out of

trouble. Peter was amazed. He remembered that he had knocked his elbow when the car was skidding from side to side. The medium explained that this was because Hawthorn wasn't used to the muscles of Gammon's body and had been a bit clumsy. Gammon remembered that he had actually had to massage his elbow when it happened. He was really thankful that Mike had bothered to come back from eternity to explain everything to him.

This wasn't the only occasion that Hawthorn slipped in and helped Gammon out of a tricky situation. Snetterton was another under-financed and -maintained circuit. It's still not a lot better. In Gammon's time it was just a World War II runway with pretensions. The straight was the actual tarmac that B29s and Lancasters had rumbled over on their way to make more ghosts in the Ruhr. At the end of it was a concrete pillbox that was supposed to be the last line of defence if the Nazis fought their way up through England and tried to take over the airfield. It has claimed at least one life and handed out a lot of bruises.

Gammon was ploughing down the straight with his foot hard to the metal. He went for the brakes, hit a particularly dodgy bit of tarmac, spun and was heading at over a 100 m.p.h. for the pill box. Gammon thought he'd had it and resigned himself to his fate.

It was not to be!

He found himself in the passenger seat, with the ignition off, the cut-out for the fuel off and the gear in neutral. He had no idea how he had done all that or how he had finished up in the passenger seat.

He went back to the medium. And yes – it was the late ex-world champion Mike Hawthorn at it again. This time he suggested that Gammon gave up motor racing before he got himself killed.

7
The Dutchman

There is a silence where no sound may be,
In the cold grave – under the deep, deep sea

Thomas Hood *Silence*

IT'S OFTEN SAID that Englishmen have the sea in their veins. This is put down to the fact that they are an island race and all Britons live within 60 miles of the sea. From this you would expect every pimply faced youth leaving school would be straight down to the nearest dock and begging to be taken on. If the way the seafarer of the eighteenth and nineteenth centuries is anything to go on, it would appear that most young men wanted to keep the saline part of the cocktail in their veins rigidly separate from the type eroding the coastlines. The pressgangs had to resort to the King's Persuader and the hope that the new recruit wouldn't become conscious until after the ship he was now sailing on, had passed the bar and was safely out to sea.

What the sea did breed was a company of villains more colourful than a company of old lags staging *HMS Pinafore* in Wandsworth Prison.

Captain Bernard Fokke was a hard and colourful man. His interest in a life on the ocean wave was sparked when, as a 15-year-old boy, working in his father's trading business, he walked down the wrong street one night and into the arms of a pressgang. They didn't bother to "persuade" him, just grabbed him by the arms and frog-marched him back to the ship. Bernard had been brought up in a loving family with a stern patriarchal figure who demanded that his sons faced up to whatever a malevolent world might throw at them and turn it to their advantage. Bernard loved the ship he found

himself aboard. The smells, the gentle rise and fall, the slap of the stays against the mast were all things he had dreamed about. He couldn't wait for the anchor to be weighed so that he could be off on his big adventure.

Unfortunately it was not to be. Not at that moment at any rate. His father, slightly perturbed that the youngster hadn't returned that night, set out to look for him and discovered that the pressgang had been recruiting in the area. He didn't waste time asking pointless questions but went straight off to see an old mate who was the local JP. JPs were big in those days. Usually the local squire or petty noble. The magistrate called up a couple of black rods or whatever and they all marched apace to the harbour and soon discovered young Bernie sitting happily on a bale and communing with the spirit of the sea. His protests that he wanted to stay were met with a clip around the ear and he was dragged back to his bedroom and locked in until the ship sailed.

But the experience stuck with him and finally his father agreed to use his influence with one of the companies he dealt with to get him a berth as a cabin boy. Bernie was overjoyed, until his ship put to sea and he found out some of the extra-curricula duties that were bound in with those of a cabin boy. He soon learned that being asked to get the last apple out of the barrel was not the straightforward chore it seemed. By the time his boat nuzzled up to his home dock again he hated every seaman on board. For most people with a choice, such experiences should have fitted him out for a job ashore – any job ashore! Unfortunately, although he hated the men, his love for the sea was undiminished. He was determined that he was going to get to a position where no man, on board or ashore, would ever force him to do anything he didn't fully endorse for the rest of his natural.

His hard, unrelenting nature didn't win him friends. But his enemies treated him with respect. If there was one thing Bernard Fokke knew about it was the sea. The sea meant ships. To be a captain meant having the trust of the merchants who relied on the shipping lanes to make their fortunes. Here Captain Fokke excelled. His ship was faster and better disciplined than any that sailed the shipping lanes. In fact, he was so fast and his deals were so profitable that the other captains darkly suggested that he had a pact with the devil. The more astute noted that he backed his wooden masts with iron plates, which meant that he could carry more sail in a higher wind velocity and therefore make more knots than with a less dangerous, more conventional set-up.

It was the beginning of the eighteenth century and the power of the British merchant fleet was beginning to be felt in every corner of the globe. Fokke set sail in the *Flying Dutchman* with a crew that hated his intestines and passengers who, to the saturnine captain, were a necessary nuisance, given ship-board on sufferance and counted somewhere between the pigs he kept in the hold for fresh meat and the weevils that added protein to the ship's biscuits. What counted was the cargo. And if he could deliver that on time – the profit! A small inconvenience was that it was "that" time of the year. The Cape of Storms was always a problem. Even in the best of weather a crewman could count on 30-foot waves – and there wasn't a lot of good weather. When Fokke came to run the straight it was decidedly "ungood" weather. Time and time again the wind and current shoved the ship back just when it appeared to be on the verge of breaking through. The crew and passengers, seasick to a man, begged him to give it a miss, come back

when 100-foot waves weren't crashing over the crow's nest and the wind had dropped to a comfortable gale.

By this time the captain had worked himself into a spitting fury and cursed everything cursable. Top of the list was his Maker who had visited such a lily-livered crew on him. In fact he got so carried away he repeatedly dared God to do his worst. Obviously the deity was having a slack time at that particular moment because He reacted. In the middle of the raging storm and pounding waves there was a moment in time when everything went calm. On the deck appeared an apparition, an emissary from on high. Fokke wasn't having any truck with supernatural beings, not while his ship and cargo were at hazard. Screaming with rage he ordered the luminescent figure to leave immediately. When it showed no signs of obeying him, the captain drew his pistol, which he always kept to hand in case he needed to persuade his crew that he knew best, and fired. Nothing happened. He tried again but again the pistol refused to fire. All this time the spectral visitor looked on placidly. When he was sure that the captain had got the point he pronounced sentence. Captain Fokke and his ship's complement were to roam the southern seas for all eternity. *The Flying Dutchman* would become a feared sight. Death would follow for any crew unlucky enough to cross its path.

It all sounded a bit over the top but every word came true. Later additions to the legend had it that the captain could go ashore every seven years to seek redemption by finding a woman so much in love with him that she would be willing to sacrifice her life. This was mainly to aid the plot-line of Wagner's Opera *Der Fliegende Hollander* in 1843 and provide a basis for James Mason to emote darkly in the 50s film *Pandora and the Flying Dutchman*.

So the legend was born and soon everyone with an ounce of imagination and spending a long time on the rail of a ship rounding the Cape began to report sightings of this haunted ship, sometimes high in the sky, riding the clouds with full sails, sometime as a shadowy figure ploughing through the

storm-tossed seas. As the frequency of the appearance of the *Flying Dutchman* increased, so did the literature. Before long, every language had its own variation and every country claimed the dyspeptic Fokke as their own – with suitable changes of name to fit the locale. In Holland he was known as "van Straaten". He was a little more phlegmatic than Fokke. No glowing angel or challenge to God. He just tried to best the Cape, got it wrong, sunk with all hands and was condemned to sail the turbulent seas forever. The Germans called him "von Falkenberg" and he has a change of location to the North Sea: not so romantic somehow. Von Falkenberg, ill advisedly, played cards with the Devil and lost. A bad scenario. When it came time to settle the wager, the Devil claimed the souls of all aboard and they were forced to sail the seas forever or until hell freezes over – whichever comes first. To set his opera apart from the penny dreadful stories in print, Wagner came up with the name "van Derdeeken" and the unlucky virgin who fell for his salty charms was Senta.

By the 1920s the story of the *Flying Dutchman* was big business. Suddenly sober, professional men were jumping up and down and swearing that they had a close encounter of the mystic kind with the haunted ship. One officer of the watch on a run from Australia to London had just rounded the Cape when about 15 minutes after midnight a strange light appeared on the port bow:

The seas were heavy and we were running before a 50 knot wind. The night was very dark and overcast with no moon. We studied the light through binoculars and the telescope and made out what appeared to be the hull of a sailing ship with two distinct masts carrying bare yards, but there was a luminous haze between the masts. There were no navigation lights and she appeared to be coming close to us and at the same speed as ourselves. When first sighted she was about 2 or 3 miles away and when she was about a half mile of us she suddenly disappeared.

There were 4 witnesses of the spectacle, the second Officer, a cadet, the helmsman and myself. I shall never forget the 2nd Officer's startled expression - "My God, Stone, it's a Ghost Ship! N.K. Stone, Fourth Officer. 26.1.1923.

This "official" sighting caused a feeding frenzy. Everybody wanted to dine out on their personal stories. Even royalty wasn't immune. Over 40 years before Stone and witnesses entered their experience into the ship's log, George, the Prince of Wales, was penning his version of the story in his private diary:

June 11th 1881: at 4 am The Flying Dutchman *crossed our bows. A strange red light as of a phantom ship all aglow in the midst of which light the masts, spars of a brig 200 yards distant stood out in strong relief. The lookout man on the forecastle reported her as close on the port bow, where also the officer of the watch from the bridge clearly saw her, as did also the quarter deck midshipman, who was sent forward to the forecastle, but found no vestige or sign whatsoever of the ship which was seen either near or right away on the horizon, the night being clear, the sea calm.*

The Prince of Wales was on a cruise with his brother, the Duke of Clarence, heir to the throne. Clarence was not the brightest of companions and was considered by many to be a diadem short of a crown. Many contemporaries even saw him as the maniacal Jack the Ripper who appeared on the streets of Whitechapel just seven years after this incident and killed off at least eight working girls. Clarence died while on holiday in Sandringham and George got the job of King. He married his brother's ex-girlfriend, Princess Mary of Teck and made her Queen Mary – after whom the famous P&O ship was named.

Since the twenties, the *Flying Dutchman* seems to have vanished. Perhaps the captain has met his virgin and retired to a little cottage on the Yorkshire coast where he can sit in an armchair and watch the churning North Sea in comfort?

8
The Hills aren't Alive

'I, from the roots of the dark thorn am hither,
And knock on the door.'

Walter de la Mare *The Ghost*

EST QUANTOXHEAD is an area of low hills that runs down to the coast of the Bristol Channel. Not a lot happens there. There's the little hamlet of St Audries, the fold in the hills that hides half a dozen houses in Weacombe Valley, a holiday camp down by the sea and a few scattered farms and houses. But if you are in the ghost-hunting business and want to combine it with a spot of camping you won't find a better place. Take St Audries itself. It has a private girls' school, now a religious retreat, a nineteenth-century rectory, a village school, a holiday camp and about 100 permanent souls. But it boasts three interesting ghosts.

In 1943–44, US servicemen were transported into England by the boatload, equipped and ready to make the trip across the English Channel and stuff it to the ungodly. A large number of them ended up in St Audries Bay Holiday Camp. The camp had been going since the 30s and consisted, at that time, of a number of wooden chalets in close formation rows. Parked high above a deserted beach, it attracted the sort of clientele that wanted to discuss literary pamphlets and sunbathe in the buff. The US army threw up a few ancillary buildings and shoehorned the bulky GIs into the chalets. A few miles down the winding road to Watchet was a British army camp. This was for a while a gunnery school. The

story has it that a young US airman flying along the coast back to his home base in Western Zoyland was unfortunate enough to wander into the range that the rooky anti-aircraft artillery men were using. They showed just how anti-aircraft they were by putting a hole in one of the wings of the little Piper Cub. With no obvious place to land, the rugged shoreline and the afforested surrounding hills not being exactly what he required, the pilot decided to push on for his home base. Not a wise decision. As he tried to fly across the Quantocks the wing finally gave up the struggle to remain an integral part of the plane and collapsed. Without a parachute and too low to use it if he had one, he just had to sit there and take it as the plane corkscrewed into the trees on the hillside. The fragile plane hit the trees and exploded just beside the walled road that separates the hills from the refined ambience of the girls' school, and spread itself over a large area. Weston Zoyland airfield assumed they had a plane down when it grew dark and there was no sign of the Piper Cub, an aircraft unsuited to night flight. The shattered woodlands were spotted the following day by a lorry driver on the milk rounds but it wasn't until late in the day that the army responded and sent out a squad to see what had happened. In the dark they found it impossible to locate the pilot's body and had to return the following day. The pilot had been thrown well clear of the debris and had lived some while before his injuries and the exposure snuffed him out.

It wasn't long before reports came in that travellers along the road in the early evening, had been startled by the sound of an aeroplane close overhead. At the point where the plane crashed the road runs between high stone walls and was, at that time, spanned by a low bridge. For a while the soundings dropped off. Then a sighting was reported to the police station in Williton a couple of miles down the road. A quarry worker claimed that as he was riding his bike along the road a plane swooped overhead and crashed into the trees. A sceptical Sergeant Combes got out his Raleigh and, sweating and swearing, peddled up the hill. He searched and found nothing but the broken trees from the Piper Cub accident. He decided that his informant was having him on and made a mental note to get even later. Manifestations dropped off for about ten years, then in the early 60s, it was decided to get rid of the low stone bridge over the road. The activity seemed to spark off a restless spirit. Demolition workers reported that not only were they spied on from the edge of the forest by a ghostly figure, in what looked like a military uniform, but somebody or something was interfering with their property. Whenever they were busy their clothes and equipment were thrown about by an intruder. Nobody liked to make the connection between the unquiet spirit of the airman in the woods and the ghostly manifestation but there was a lot of talk about how quiet the area was and how birds never sang there. And, of course, no poacher was ever able to get a good dog anywhere near the place. There appears to have been no reported sightings in recent years. Has the ghostly airman at last been repatriated to become one of the dozens of aeriel sightings on airfields reported annually in the States?

Less than half a mile away on the top of the hill behind the quarry there used to be a stand of fir trees. They stood alone, in a majestic circle surrounded by a low earthworks. Only the earthworks remain. The view is magnificent. To the north the hills open up to reveal the wide expanse of the Bristol Channel. On a clear day the dark horizon reveals the Welsh coastline with Cardiff slap-bang in the middle. Over to the east Flat Holme and Steep Holme. Those mysterious slabs of rock in the centre of the Channel stand in companionable grandeur. Just what was practised within the circle of trees is a mystery. The remains stand only a couple of hundred yards from the old rectory, now a mental institution, in the valley beside the walled road. Whatever mysterious goings-on went on in the trees has left an echo. Faint lights and even fainter bodies were seen quite frequently before the war. Since then only occasionally has anyone been startled by the ethereal figures. It might have something to do with the bomb that was dropped, only a hundred yards away, by a German bomber that, for some unfathomable reason, thought he was over Cardiff and unleashed his lethal load.

But if you're in the district and looking for an unspoiled place to kip, you could do worse than pitch your tent in the circle of stones and see if you get supernatural urges to dance.

The third apparition ropes in the bloody Judge Jeffries. Sedgemoor, the scene of the Duke of Monmoth's rag-tail army getting well and truly stuffed by the trained troops of James II in 1685, is only a score or so miles to the east. Sedgemoor is another place where ghostly armies are said to hang around for eternity asking such searching questions as "What do we do now?" or "Who won?" There's another story about a soldier who was captured by a band of Royalists looking for a fun night out. After giving their captive a playful beating they offered him a choice. Suck the business end of a musket

or make the chicken run. If the soldier made the old oak by the Sedgemoor Drain he was home free. The man embraced the faint hope that he could outrun a fusillade of bullets and set off. Miraculously he survived to get to the tree. Then he made the cardinal mistake of stopping. The Royalists proved what wags they were by shooting him anyway. On the anniversary of the Battle of Sedgemoor the sound of shouts, the thunder of horses' hooves, and the rattle of musket fire can still be heard. And, if you're really close, it is said you can hear the rasping breath of the poor soldier as he races toward the tree that he thought would mean sanctuary. There is a further tragedy concocted supernaturally by the horrific happening on Sedgemoor. The soldier's fiancée, hearing of her lover's death, couldn't stand the thought of living without a pension and drowned herself in the Sedgemoor Drain. After the pounding horses, whistle of bullets and panting breath, the ghost of the maiden appears, wan and misty in the moonlight just to point up that it wasn't only the men at the front who suffered.

But there's more. After the Battle of Sedgemoor the lanes were full of fleeing peasants and noblemen trying to get home before they were missed and someone earned themselves a bob or two by pointing the finger. One country gent had thoughtfully kept his carriage and six close to hand. It was useful as a triumphal vehicle if the day went the Monmoth way or, as in this case, as a reasonably comfortable and fast way of deserting the luckless Duke. Plummeting through the narrow lanes the driver rocked around a bend to be confronted by the obligatory old crone carrying the statutory bundle of wood on her bowed back. The driver had the choice of trying to avoid her and risk upsetting his master's repose or running her over. No contest. As the old woman lay broken and dying she laid a curse on all drivers who drive carelessly along country lanes and run down defenceless old crones.

Since that fatal night there have been many accidents and near accidents on the spot. Sometimes it's the old dear herself who appears momentarily in the headlights of a speeding car. At others it is the cursed coach and six driven by the driver with an early case of road-rage.

9
Sweeney Todd
(The Demon Barber of Fleet Street)

I knew a man once did a girl in -

T.S. Eliot *Sweeney Agonistes*

FLEET STREET, in the heart of London, earned itself a pretty spectacular reputation as the broadcaster of sensational stories. Most of these came from places far removed from the busy, traffic-clogged street that headed out of town via Aldgate. But there is one story that attaches itself to the street like luckless flies to sticky paper: the sensational business practices of Sweeney Todd. Todd, in the generally accepted version of the story, ran a barbers shop in Fleet Street. The customers coming through the door equated neither with Todd's lifestyle nor the number of customers going out of the door. The reason was simple. His partner in crime ran a very lucrative business next door selling pork pies. Again anyone trying to get a profit and loss sheet going on the trade would have had a few problems. Like how can you sell pork pies without actually buying any pork. The answer was simple.

Sweeny Todd had a special chair in his barber's shop. When the pork-pie ingredients in Mrs Lovett's shop ran low the barber picked a particular succulent customer in need of a shave and then ran his well-stropped blade so close that it severed the jugular. A quick flip of a concealed lever and the prospective pork-pie filling tipped backwards out of the chair, through a trapdoor, down a chute and onto Madame Lovett's chopping block. With the pickings from the pocket of the unlucky pie-fillings and the secondhand price for a suit of clothes the cooperative was very lucrative. Especially when the profit from the pies was counted in. Very lucrative! It all seemed so easy that the cook got careless. Imagine the horror when a customer bit into one of the tasty pies and found a ring, still with a finger attached, in his mouth. The demon barber of Fleet Street and his partner Mrs Lovett of the famous pie shop soon lost their franchise.

Of course, there's nothing ghostly about Sweeney Todd. Maybe the actor who played him in the 1936 version of the story, Tod Slaughter, might be described as out of this world. His acting was always a little ripe but in *Sweeney Todd, the Demon Barber of Fleet Street*, he went above and beyond anything he had done before. Probably beyond anything anyone had ever done before.

As remarkable as the story is there does seem to have been a real-life barber who did the business with cut throat and piecrust and died to leave a ghost. His name was Jarman and he lived just up the road from what is now Heathrow airport in the little village of Colnebrook. His place of business was not a barber's shop but an ancient hostelry, the Ostrich Inn. The variation on the tip-up barber chair was a specially hinged bed. In the kitchen below, a huge cauldron of water was kept bubbling. When a suitable guest presented himself, Jarman came over all oily innkeeper and bowed the unlucky person (he was an early example of PC – he didn't make any distinction between male and female) into what he assured them was the best room in the house. He left a flagon of ale and a keg or so of rum on tap and retired below while the unsuspecting guest tucked into the freebies and congratulated himself on finding such a marvellous establishment. When he, in an advanced state of sozzledness, finally collapsed onto the bed, Jarman was on hand to prepare him for the next world. A sharp knife across the windpipe to make sure the shock of plunging into the boiling water didn't cause the victim to become unnecessarily noisy, a tug on the lever and the bed canted up and deposited the gory body into the cauldron.

Business was good for quite a while. The fiendish landlord and his cordon bleu wife had more luck than they deserved. One of their intended victims actually escaped but there must have been something about the place he liked – probably the smell of cooking seeping up from below. Whatever, a short time later he was ringing the bell on the reception desk and booking in again. Even demanded the same room as before. Again he survived. Jarman and his missus must have wondered what they could do to prevent their pork-pie filling spilling his offal to the local fuzz. When he appeared in the doorway for a third time they couldn't believe it, especially when he demanded the same room again. This time Jarman made no mistake and the frequent traveller became the residents' dinner. The demon hotelier was overwrought by his experience: it wasn't the sort of thing he was used to and he and his fragrant spouse sat long into the night trying to figure out the basic psychology of the pork pies browning in the oven. They were so caught up with their philosophising about the way of the world that they forgot basic hygiene and didn't clean up. But it was the horse getting restless in the stable that was the giveaway. Why they didn't branch out into a specialised line of *chevaux* pies isn't recorded. Whatever happened, the local Reeve felt called upon to investigate and discovered the hinged bed. It was not easy to explain. With the boiling cauldron immediately below he could have claimed it was an en suite bathroom, but it doesn't seem to have occurred to either Jarman or his wife.

By the time the Reeve had got through with his investigation he believed that at least 60 guests had left without paying their bills. Instead of commiserating with the Jarmans on the iniquities of the hotelier's nightmare, the moonlight flit, he arrested them. The local JP, probably in a foul mood because he missed his special pork pies, sentenced them to death.

If there is one place that deserves to be haunted it's the Ostrich Inn. The good news is that it is. Trouble is that so many souls were liberated within its walls that it's impossible to tell just whose shade stalks the fatal bedroom. Is it Jarman, looking for more throats to cut? Or his wife, made redundant by the lack of on-the-hoof pie filler and trying to find out what had happened to the supply? Maybe one or more of the guests haunts the killing corridor, still bemused by the fact that he went to bed drunk and woke up in the bowel of the local JP.

Then again, it could be the third-time-unlucky guest looking for his horse.

10
The Man in Grey

What! Has this thing appear'd again tonight?

William Shakespeare *Hamlet*

THEATRE GHOSTS ARE, of course, two a penny. Or should that be Ecu now? Whatever the small change, ghosts, probably getting energy from certain leading actors' overweening *almas*, like the theatre. The one that gets my vote is the Man in Grey who hangs out at the Theatre Royal in Drury Lane. This isn't one of your faded, retiring shades. He gets really involved, appearing at rehearsals and encouraging the actors when the going gets hard. During the performance he appears on the balcony in the end seat of row D. The number of people who claim to see him is legion. Most haven't just seen him once but a number of times. So far nobody has managed to take a photograph; probably the warning not to use cameras in the auditorium during the performance is enough to keep the law-abiding theatregoers in check. Descriptions of the astral first-nighter are detailed and amazingly similar. It seems that he is young, with an athletic figure and a pleasant, broadly smiling visage. His clothes do tend to set him apart from the rest of the audience although, with the popularising of Regency vampires, it is increasingly possible to meet up with punters in fancy dress. This dress-circle Johnny wears a beautifully ruffled silk shirt, a three-cornered hat like a true highwayman, highly polished riding boots, a sword and a flowing grey cloak. His appearance at a rehearsal or a matinée is usually the augury for a successful run. There is obviously some sort

of paraphysical contract for his appearances as he is never seen at the evening performance. Never is not exactly right. There have been a few reports of him appearing in his favourite seat the night before the notices go up for the premature end of a show. It's hard to get anything definite on this as by the time the notice goes up there are not enough people in the audience to report a sighting.

Although the ghost does seem to interact with his surroundings to a certain degree it appears that he is bound to a routine of sorts. For instance, he never turns up at an inopportune moment in the leading lady's dressing room. Like any inveterate theatregoer he starts off in the bar in the upper circle, glides to the far side of the theatre, takes the stairs to the back of the auditorium, and crosses back to the other side, goes through the door and down the stairs – then disappears through the wall. His movements are described as languid and unhurried. When he does break his routine and take a seat it is always the same one. Whatever happened in life, it was obviously bound up with the theatre. He particularly likes a musical, it seems. Just before the Second World War, the cast of *The Dancing Years* was on stage for a photo-call. A great opportunity, you might think, for a professional photograph. The spectre of row D did his bit. Watched by the entire cast he appeared at the back of the auditorium on the upper circle, stood for a moment as if approving the cast then did his usual perambulations and disappeared. The photographer hadn't heard that old dictum that you don't watch – you shoot. Another great opportunity for visual evidence lost. It was a pity that the charlady who had a close encounter wasn't carrying a camera instead of a mop when she was "doing" the upper circle. Being just a menial and outside the lovey set she hadn't been told about the mysterious Man in Grey. The poor old dear saw this poncey looking character sitting at the end of row D and thought he was an actor in costume. Jealous of her territory she approached the intruder, set on asserting her authority and banishing him back to his own region. Imagine the consternation when her target, without even looking at her, melted in his seat and disappeared. When her phlegm was restored on the wave of numerous cups of tea she told her co-workers what she had witnessed and was slightly miffed when they off-handedly claimed to have seen the apparition on many occasions.

Another near encounter happened when *Oklahoma* was playing. An elegant-looking character in a grey cloak, a cocked hat, ruffled shirt and shining riding boots was seen to enter the auditorium by a number of first-nighters waiting for the doors to open. They assumed that it was a member of the cast getting in position for one of those "out of the audience" surprises that theatre directors love so much. They think it binds the bums on seats to the performers behind the footlights. When the audience was finally let in there was no sign of the man in the fancy outfit.

It seems that seeing the mysterious Man in Grey is included in the ticket price. In fact, if you don't see him it is almost a basis for getting a refund. During the war the theatre was taken over by ENSA, the entertainment company responsible for providing shows for what were charmingly called "the boys at the front!" At that time

London was very much on the front line with thousands of tons of high explosives raining down on the capital nightly. In spite of this it was the focus of most servicemen on leave and the theatre in Drury Lane with its dance halls cafés and obliging ladies was crammed to capacity. Neither the bombs nor the unwinding military deterred the restless spirit. He was sighted by a number of servicemen and staff who had never heard about the Man in Grey. None of these had cameras either.

With the alleged frequency of the phantom's appearances it is incredible that nobody has so far come up with anything that might be judged a photograph. Even experienced members of the ghostbusting fraternity haven't come up with anything that a less than spectral man going over Tower Bridge on a Number 11 bus would get excited about. Harry Price, the man in the tight-fitting double-breasted suit and fedora who claimed to be the leading ghosthunter in the fifties, only managed a "bluish-grey light" and an "impression" of a limping man. And these experts turned up with camera, vibration detectors, thermometers and all the other paraphernalia that never seems to actually detect a ghostly presence. Maybe that judgement is a little harsh. They did come up with something. Something that, by its negativity, prompted them to claim that they had made a breakthrough and detected something. The sort of evidence that goes down big with kangaroo courts and Sherlock Holmes enthusiasts. Most of the exposed film was blank except a couple of frames that had pinpoints of light. Most people, when they get this sort of result, blame either the chemist who developed them or their other half who wielded the camera. Ghosthunters are made of sterner stuff. They wrote it up in their journals and claimed a major breakthrough into the afterlife.

There is some evidence to confirm the Man in Grey's presence in the Theatre Royal. Real forensic evidence this time. Over a hundred years ago, in 1874, when the theatre was being refurbished, a workman smashed down a wall and discovered a hidden cupboard behind it. Propped up in a corner, covered by the dust of ages, was a skeleton in the remains of a grey suit and boots that had been all but devoured by the rats. Sticking out of the skeletal ribs was a workmanlike knife. Was it a critic who went one adjective too far? Or an actor with an ambitious understudy? Or maybe a playwright who was the victim of a bad case of plagiarism? Nobody will ever know now. Unless you happen to be sitting at the end of row D in the upper circle and a man in a fancy-dan outfit sits beside you. Don't bother to try and get a picture. Ask him who his tailor is and all will be revealed.

The elegant Man in Grey is most well known in his spectral state, but another apparition who has appeared to a number of people was better known in his corporeal form. Dan Leno is always described as a comic genius. Especially by comedian Roy Hudd. The claim has even been made that the charming Roy is actually Leno reincarnate. There is always that suggestion implicit in his championship of the little man. Roy even had an off-theatre experience that surely binds him to the ex-comedian more than most? Some years ago he was invited to dinner at a friend's house in Brixton. When he arrived outside he had what is generally called "a turn." He had never been to the house before but instantly recognised it. It had figured in a recurring dream for years. In the dream he explored the house and always finished up in the cellar. Before he woke up he was aware that the cellar was lined with mirrors. His hosts were more than a little surprised when he went through the house describing what he would find before actually opening the door. Up until that time Roy claims no special interest in Leno but, inspired by the fulfilment of his dream he dug into the archives and became an expert on Dan Leno when he found that the comedian had lived in the

Brixton house and that he always rehearsed his dance routines in a circle of mirrors.

Hudd worked up the brief encounter with the past into a television documentary with himself taking on the leading role. Roy Hudd never claimed to have actually made contact with the ghost of one of the most famous pantomime dames in the history of the theatre but there are others who do. Stanley Lupino, father of the actress Ida, for instance. He was sitting in his dressing room, sipping a medicinal brandy and waiting for the five-minute call when he became aware that he was not alone. He carefully lowered his brandy glass and blinked. Walking across his dressing room towards the door was a man. The visitor appeared to walk through the door without opening it. That looked a bit dodgy for a start but Lupino was willing to believe that the brandy had helped to misinterpret the sequence of events. So he casually asked the stage-door man if anyone had been in to see him. Put on his mettle because of the implied slur on the efficiency of his guardianship of the sacred stage door, the keeper replied that nobody who shouldn't have had crossed the forbidden portals. Lupino resolved to take more water with his brandy in future. It didn't help. A couple of days later Lupino was sitting at his dressing table putting on his stage make-up when he became aware of another image beside him in the mirror. It was the unmistakable white-featured Dan Leno. That was enough for Stanley. He told the ASM he wasn't feeling too good and left the theatre.

Leno's after-echo is what might be called peripatetic. Unlike most remnants of a life misspent, Leno put it about a bit and used to make the odd appearance at the Collins Music Hall on Islington Green before it had a fatal encounter with a demolition ball. Here he wasn't content to just hang around and frighten anyone using his old dressing room At the music hall he became a ghostly critic, watching performances and making it very obvious if he thought the show or the performance of any of the actors was not up to snuff.

Dan Leno also took an occasional ethereal bow at the Olympia Theatre in Dublin. Such theatrical luminaries as Jessie Mathews and Dame Edith Evans have claimed to hear Leno practising his famous clog dance and been aware of his presence at rehearsals.

There's just one other ghost at the theatre who's worth mentioning. This one's no shrinking violet hovering around in the upper circle. This one likes to strut his stuff where it matters – centre stage. The belligerent shade is said to belong to an actor who killed another in an argument in the Green Room.

Charles Macklin was not one of your fun-loving vagabonds. When he was in one of his frequent bad tempers it was a good time to be somewhere else. A fact that fellow thespian, Tom Hallam, would have done well to recognise. He was resting in the green room between performances when Macklin burst in and accused him of using his wig. Hallam stoutly denied poaching his accuser's syrup and tried to leave. Macklin wasn't having that. He swung the heavy malacca cane that he always carried since one of his leading ladies had told him it made him look impressive. The cane certainly made an impression on Hallam. It knocked out his eye. Poor old Hallam, wigless and sightless, died as a result of the injury. You might be pardoned for thinking that having a fatal eye-injury over a secondhand hairpiece might be enough to create a ghost. You might – but you'd be wrong. It's not the victimised Hallam who commandeers the stage before curtain-up but the aggressive Macklin. Could it be that his restless soul still searches for his missing toupee?

11
London Bridge

Thus march we playing to our latest rest...

Sir Walter Raleigh

EVERYONE KNOWS the story of the gormless American millionaire who came to London and put a bid in for London Bridge. Everyone was gobsmacked. Who could possibly want the ugly concrete edifice? And what could they do with it that a demolition ball couldn't do better? But if the American wanted to buy it and ship it to the Arizona desert along with a load of London buses, taxis and other paraphernalia that had long passed its sell-by date, who were the poor unimaginative Brits to argue? The surprise in London that they were getting rid of it was not as great as when the jumble of steel and concrete was put together in the US. The buyer had expected a glorious Victorian edifice of crenellated towers and a bridge that could be raised and lowered by fascinating nineteenth-century mechanisms. What they got was the unexciting nineteenth-century concrete bridge that connected the south to the City. The confusion had been caused by the purchaser's non-understanding of what he had bought. Whenever he saw a representative picture of London it usually displayed the triple icons of the Tower of London, Big Ben and Tower Bridge! The mistake was easy to make but hard to rectify. Once London had got itself shot of London Bridge it didn't want it back. So

there, on the borders of Lake Havasu City, Arizona, in 1971, the wrong bridge was officially opened by a cynical Sir Peter Studd, Lord Mayor of London and Jack Williams, the Governor of Arizona. Everybody put on a brave face and nobody mentioned the cock-up.

That's the story. Probably apocryphal but one that gives us a warm feeling of superiority when it's told. The bridge was placed in the setting of a "typical" English village as visualised by the average American complete with red buses, taxis and the occasionally capering cockney Pearly King. The Governor wanted more. But what could you do with a rusty old bridge? Fate – or the PR department – came to the aid of the Arizona white elephant. Ghostly figures were soon to be seen strolling in the moonlight across the bridge. What about that? Photographs? Well, wouldn't you know it. Jamming cameras and spoiled film won the day yet again. But all was not lost. The film industry, with help from the State of Arizona, decided that the misty figures promenading across the bridge and seen only by a privileged few, were probably shipped over with the bridge and that meant that there was a 99.9% chance that Jack the Ripper had made the voyage as well. Everybody knows that London Bridge was one of Jack's favourite haunts. On the map it's only a quarter of an inch away from Whitechapel. Extrapolating that premise to its ultimate conclusion put the Ripper in the little town of Havasu, out of his depth but relying on basic instincts to perform hurried genital operations in the buses and keep him out of the hands of the police.

A ghost haunting a strange land is also trotted out for inspection in the 1936, London Films' *The Ghost Goes West*. In a way it actually pre-echoes the London Bridge fiasco but instead of the demonic Jack the Ripper, it is a rather sweet Scottish laird played by the diffident Robert Donat who does the haunting. It was the first English-language film for French *maître* René Clair. It got a slow start but in the long run has become a bit of a minor classic. As usual in films you get a chance to see the actual making of the ghost. This one is spawned in the mid-18th century when the laird, played by Donat – head of the Murdochs – is insulted by a neighbouring laird. He springs to the defence of his honour but unfortunately dies before satisfaction can be given. This, obviously, is enough to keep any laird worth his kilt earthbound. Jump

a couple of centuries. The new laird, also played by Donat, is in the creditor-dodging business. It looks as if the final disgrace is going to befall his family and they are going to have to pay the tailor when the obligatory, loud-mouthed, filthy rich American, Eugene Pallete, jingles the castle bell. Equally obligatory, he has a beautiful daughter, played by Jean Arthur, who makes Donat's eye come all over watery. Pallete offers a deal. He wants to buy up the castle and ship it back to the US and rebuild it on his Florida homestead. With an eye to a feudal title for his love-stuck daughter, Pallete offers Donat a job – as caretaker. Either the sea air or the Florida blue rinses awakens Donat's filmic ancestor who is not at all pleased to be playing apparition to a colonial and starts to make his ghostly presence felt. But being an echo in stone for half a dozen generations has mellowed the irascible Scottish phantom and he gradually gets around to helping out his hapless descendent in a spot of ethereal wooing.

No such happy ending has so far been reported for London's Bridge now marooned in the Arizona desert.

12
Edward II

As the soul leaves the body torn and bruised,
As the mind deserts the body it has used.

T.S. Eliot *La Figlia Che Piange*

IF THERE WAS ever a castle that was built to be haunted and a king born to haunt it – it was Berkeley and Edward II. In a list of moody monarchs he would be well up in the top ten. His moodiness would have been understood in the modern-day world of absentee fathers and sparing the rod and breeding a generation of glue-sniffing joyriders. Daddy, Edward I, was a big man in every sense. He knew what was what and went for it. When he wasn't sticking it to the ungodly on a crusade he was up to the grieves in Welsh blood hacking down Barons or whacking the Scots. With the vassal state of Wales on his shield, he forced them to bend a knee to his indolent son, Edward II, who became the first Prince of Wales, and was born, appropriately, in Carnarvon Castle. Edward II's ideas for a happy life were markedly different from the old man's. Little Eddie liked lying in bed, playing doctors with the other boys and dressing up. His mother, Eleanor of Castile, had heard about the English Disease and thought that her son's predilection for silk next to his skin and not washing was natural. By the time he was old enough to be noticed by his father, Edward II ruled over a court of vapid young men with a tendency to stand provocatively with one hand on their hip and a moue of displeasure on their lips.

Edward I wasn't going to have that. He was laying claim to being the final Hammer of the Scots and he wasn't going to have a son of his keeping company with a gang of shirtlifters. So he girded up Edward junior's loins with chainmail and horsehair Y-fronts and led him north to meet William Wallace and Robert the Bruce. Junior wasn't amused although it did bring him into contact with a lot of rough men who weren't too particular where they got their rocks off. Even the fruits of the field began to pall after a while and he got homesick for his special friend, the delightful Piers de Gaveston. Papa Edward was a problem but when he conveniently laid down and died, Edward II, now King, didn't hang about but lit out for London and the delights of Piers and his special coterie of friends.

Although Edward might be a key player for the other team he still had his kingly duty to the Crown to perform. A match was made with Isabella, daughter of Philip IV of France. Philip might be known as "the Fair" but he took an instant dislike to his new son-in-law and renewed his ties with the beleaguered Scots. Propelled by his strong-minded mother Edward agreed to go through with the union but couldn't resist creating his favourite, de Gaveston, Earl of Cornwall and leaving him in charge when he left for France to sort out his nuptials. This got the landed gentry in a really bad humour and didn't do the King's relationship with his mum much good either.

Edward's affection for Piers and the dear boy's stupidity caused problems for both: problems that were to be fatal for the Gascon and deeply hurtful for his royal *amorata*. The barons kept kicking de Gaveston out of the country and the King kept bringing him back. It was a situation waiting for a Gordian solution and the Lords found it. They executed Piers de Gaveston and waited to see what his friend would do. The King cried a lot and was as spiteful as he could be to all those who had supported the notion of terminating his relationship with his favourite. They weren't too worried. They had the tacit backing of Edward's mother Eleanor. So Edward decided it was time to give the Scots a good seeing to. Since his father's death, the Highlanders had been getting too cocky by half. Edward gathered a large army and minced north. Things didn't go the King's way. For one thing in the seven years since Edward I's death the Scots, under the leadership of Robert the Bruce, had learned a thing or two and, for another, the King's army was led by the favourite who had replaced dear Piers. They now spent their youth strutting about strumming a madrigal instead of tilting a lance. Once Edward saw which way the blood was running he remembered duties further south and didn't stop until he touched home base. His Kingly discomfiture inspired the Welsh and the Irish to try and shake off his jaundiced hand but they weren't as successful as the Scots.

This was the beginning of the ride to his painful destiny in Berkeley Castle. First he had Thomas the Earl of Lancaster giving him a hard time. With the aid of his new pet, Hugh le Depenser, he got rid of Lancaster. He then dallied with the idea of putting down the saucy Scots but again met with a lack of success.

Now his wife began to get into her stride. She had stood by and watched him make a fool of himself for the last time. She sent a letter to her brother, Charles IV of France, asking to come home. It was a bit awkward: there were covenants and treaties that were all bound up with her marriage to the throne of England. She persuaded him that it was time to get English feet off French soil and he claimed back all the land the English Crown held in France. Edward swallowed the bait and sent his wife off to her brother to try and make him see sense. What Edward didn't know was that Isabella was having a bit of a ding-dong with one of his straighter nobles, Roger de Mortimer. Her hidden agenda was to raise an army in France while de Mortimer did his bit of subversion in England and then meet up on a convenient bit of coast in the south of England.

Everything went according to plan and Isabella and Roger marched on London, overthrew the King and killed his band of favourites. Even Isabella balked at the thought of combining regicide with murder – after all she was a good Catholic girl whatever troubles her family might be having with the Pope. To show her goodwill towards her husband she promised that, if he abdicated, she would not touch a hair of his body.

Now, on a calm autumn night when the conditions are right, you can hear the unworldly screams of Edward II as his wife fulfils her pledge. In a small room on the first floor the incapable King relives for eternity, or for as long as anyone hears his screams, the horrendous pain of his barbarous death. A death that makes your sphincter twitch just thinking about it.

A brazier was taken to his room in the dark of night and he was hauled out of his bed and made to watch as a poker was heated up "till it was white hot." Then he was stretched out, face down on the table and a cow's horn with the tip cut off was stuck up his bum. Then, without ceremony or a chance to recant his sins, the fiery rod was thrust deep into his vitals and held there while he screamed himself to death. Even Edward II didn't

deserve that but I guess Isabella felt the warm glow of honour served. After all there wasn't a hair on her husband's corpse that had been harmed.

Berkeley Castle was the scene of the King's death throes and gave us a royal ghost that still haunts the corridor and galleries when he's not reenacting his final scene. But what of his favourite Piers de Gaveston?

Well, it seems that when the nobles, disenchanted with Edward's choice of counsellors, decided to get rid of Piers de Gaveston, they took him to Scarborough Castle, well out of the way of any opposition the King's supporters might mount, and chopped off his head. The preening Piers couldn't believe that anyone could be so gauche as to separate his beautiful head from his divine body and refused to accept death. Now he haunts the battlements and halls of the old castle and vents his pent-up spite on anyone he doesn't like.

The other restless spirit bound by the awful death of Edward is his wife Isabella. She appears to be quite at home in the ancient Porchester Castle. Probably finds company in a lot of ghosts who have their own territory to haunt. The castle was built by the Romans and even claims Pontius Pilate as a guest. And we all know what a lot of hand-wringing the unforgettable governor of Judea went in for. The spectre guest book is impressive. King John, between harassing serfs and giving barons a bad time, stayed there. Richard II, Henry I, the luckless Edward II, Edward III, Henry VIII and even a putative witch and soon to be headless Anne Boleyn, made pithy remarks in the visitors' book.

It just goes to show what a burden is placed on us parents. If only Edward I had been there for the boy who knows how it would all have ended.

13
Possession and Danny Kaye

When by thy scorne, O murdresse, I am dead,
And that thou thinkst thee free
From all solicitation from mee,
Then shall my ghost come to thy bed ...

John Donne *The Apparition*

CHARACTER CHANGES CAN be the result of all sorts of things. A couple of beers can do it for some folk; others need something heavier, like a traffic incident that turns mild-mannered professor into a badly painted Hulk. For some it's a bad reaction to something they have eaten or a blow across the ear with an aluminium baseball bat. Then there are the spirits. Not those from an optic but the sort that made Linda Blair's bed a less than salubrious place to loiter in during the making of *The Exorcist*. Possession comes in all spooks and spectres but, Old Nick himself aside, most of the green spittle, pustule-popping special effects are done by relatives trying to get their own back or someone cheesed off with the disturbance to their post-mortal existence. As an example, take Esther Cox.

She lived in Nova Scotia in 1898 with her elder sister Olive and her husband Dan Teed. She was 19 and still shared a bed with her 22-year-old sister Jennie. There wasn't a lot to do in the little township of Amherst so the suggestion that there was an invasion of mice came as a big, well biggish, event. It was still a fresh topic of conversation so when Esther felt something stir under the sheets she gave a half-strangled shriek and leapt out

of bed. Her sister, probably dreaming of something really exciting, like what hymns would be selected for the service on Sunday and whether she really believed in the immaculate conception, was not amused. Esther insisted that she help her search the room. Zilch! This in itself was unusual but they were tired and decided that Esther's scream had driven the immediate mouse population underground.

This was just a curtain raiser. The following night Jennie and Esther went to bed, the mouse incident forgotten until they both heard a rustling sound that seemed to come from a box under the bed. Mice were again targeted as the culprits and the girls pulled out the boxes with the idea of stamping on a few diminutive heads and getting a decent night's sleep. It didn't work out that way. As soon as the box was out from under the bed it took on a life of its own and whizzed up towards the ceiling. Both girls hit a note that an opera diva could only admire and dived back under the bedclothes. Daniel, the brother-in-law, arrived barefoot. As happens in all the best hauntings, by the time he got there whatever it was that was motivating the box had decided to play it cool. Daniel laughed at the girls and accused them of sharing a common nightmare. Esther and Jennie weren't too pleased at having their levitating box dismissed in such an arbitrary fashion and the following day passed very quietly. When it was time to go to bed, tactfully, nobody made any reference to what had happened the previous night.

It was about a quarter past ten and everyone had dropped peacefully off to sleep. Without warning Esther leapt out of bed, taking the blanket with her, and stood transfixed in the middle of the room. Jennie was annoyed at first but when she saw what had happened to her sister her annoyance turned to horror. Esther's long dark curls had transformed into a bursting halo of hair around her head. Her normally pale face was scarlet and puffy and her eyes bulged like a couple of fried eggs. Again Daniel was first on the spot. This time there was no disappearing spectre or rodent. Esther stood in the centre of the room, a low keening forcing its way past livid, bloated lips. As the sisters and Daniel watched they were terrified to see that Esther was blowing up like a Michelin man before their eyes. Olive was the first to pull her wits together and went to the younger girl. She didn't seem to recognise her but stared at her fiercely from the depths of her bulging face. As Olive tried to think of a way to comfort her tormented sister a thunderclap clashed out, shaking the house. Esther appeared to realise where she was. Three more thunderclaps shook the house, terrifying the little gathering in the bedroom. Esther gave a little moan and, as her family watched, slowly deflated until she was her old natural self again. She gave the others a sad little smile than sank peacefully to the floor in a swoon. They put her back to bed and sat up with her. Esther seemed unmoved by the extraordinary events and, after a good night's sleep, woke up and went about whatever she normally went about as if nothing out of the ordinary had happened. The rest watched her carefully for signs

that whatever it was that had happened the night before didn't happen again. By bedtime the atmosphere was pretty tense and affected everyone but Esther. Jennie spent the night listening to the regular breathing of her sister and tried to convince herself that the traumas of the last few nights were over. Nothing happened. The following night was also peaceful. When the third night passed without incident Jennie was prepared to accept that whatever it was that had been affecting Esther was a thing of the past. It was a case of "just when I thought it was all over ... " Jennie was jerked violently from sleep when the bedclothes were ripped off the bed, flew through the air and somehow attached themselves to the ceiling. By this time both the women had become well practised screamers and once more Daniel Teed beat his wife to the bedroom. Esther was at it again. Standing in the middle of the room, keening and visibly swelling up. Dan tried to pull down the bedclothes to wrap around his obviously disturbed sister-in-law. Without success. Every time he tried to pull them away from the ceiling it was as if a supernatural force pulled in the opposite direction. When he persisted pillows flew, of their own volition, at his head. Daniel was not happy. Under normal circumstances he prided himself that he could cope with anything. Telekinetic pillows and unseen supernatural forces playing tug-of-war were not something he considered that he should be expected to take on. He was saved from a public display of funk by a tremendous clap of thunder. Esther relaxed and again sunk silently to the floor. This was something that Teed was not prepared to take on without professional advice. So he called in his doctor, Dr Carritte. Carritte was a fun man. He was willing to go along with a good joke as much as anyone, especially if there was a fee in it and he wasn't made to look too much like the archetypal village doctor on laudanum overload. He didn't smile for long. As he was bending over examining Esther, the pillow under her head shifted violently with no apparent cause. He tried to plump it up and put it back under her head but the pillow had a will of its own and refused to be tamed. The doctor began to wish he had taken a slug of laudanum before he left home after all. What did it matter if he was a country bumpkin? A scratching sound behind him had the hair on the back of his neck vibrating. It wasn't doing too much for the equanimity of the others in the room either. Like an unrehearsed bit of business from an Abbott and Costello film, the doctor slowly turned and, step-by-step, backed off. On the wall at the foot of the bed, before their horrified eyes, a message was being crudely etched into the plaster accompanied by a cacophony of bangs, rattles and a super-tonal crying and screaming. The message read: *"Esther Cox, you are mine to kill!"* Not something to read when you are in a delicate state of health. Esther felt the same way. She fainted. The doctor tried to put a scientific slant on what had happened, as befits a man of medicine, and left hurriedly.

Fortified, no doubt by a draft of nanny's friend, he was back early in the morning. He wasn't too sure what was going on but he rather suspected that someone was having a go at him. As soon as he arrived Esther told him about the latest manifestations. She was in the kitchen making herself a bite to eat when, from out of nothing, a bit of four by two whacked her across the back of the head. "Aaaah!" thought the doctor, "A chance to investigate an on-the-spot occurrence" – or something like that. He directed Esther to show him exactly where she had been attacked. Esther led the way to the kitchen but moved warily. The doctor pushed her aside and went into the kitchen. There wasn't any wood about but, before he could duck, he was bombarded by flying potatoes. As he staggered back to the protection of the doorway he heard a loud, rumbling sound from deep underground. The rest of the day passed peacefully enough. The doctor waited

until Esther retired to bed, then hung around for a while chatting to Daniel Teed. He finally decided that nothing was going to happen that night so whistled up his horse and left. His housekeeper was very sceptical of his reason for staying at the Teed house so long and neglecting his other patients. Probably thought he was in danger of blowing the doctor-patient relationship and finishing up on a fizzer at the BMA. Carritte felt called upon to reassure her that his interest in the female members of the Cox family was purely professional. His housekeeper, slightly mollified by his protestations, fixed him a sandwich and a glass of buttermilk and went to bed. He was about to follow her, to his own monastic chamber as far as we know, when Dan Teed banged on the door. Shortly after the doctor left Esther had come all over peculiar and collapsed. The doc picked up his bag and went back to the beleaguered house.

He was relieved to find that the much-put-upon Esther was suffering from diphtheria. Not much he could do about it but at least he could name it. When he left the house he was in for a surprise. A crowd had gathered. Carritte's housekeeper had put the word around about the haunting and her boss's part in it and in Nova Scotia anything out of the ordinary merits an award. Even coupling dogs get a round of applause and a write-up in the local journal.

During Esther's illness whatever had been plaguing the house took a holiday. She convalesced with another married sister in the south, and Jennie, Olive and Daniel could get a regular eight hours' sleep without disturbance. It was the proverbial lull before the storm. Refreshed, Esther came home. And suddenly she was hearing voices. Nothing wrong with that. Even St Joan heard voices. Perhaps the same ones. Joan finished up on a funeral pyre before being decently dead and now Esther was being threatened with the same sort of fiery fate. The voices threatened that they were going to burn down the house and everyone in it. Just to show that they weren't kidding, lighted Swan Vestas started raining down from the ceiling. The shower lasted for about ten minutes and Daniel had his work cut out keeping the flames under control.

Jennie now moved centre stage. She was hearing voices, she had a direct line to the poltergeist that was causing all the trouble. Jennie did the whole bit, letters on the table, every one holding hands and an ethereal question and answer session. With a series of questions which could only be answered "yes" or "no", a feat that would have made a barrister proud, she drew out the intelligence that it was Esther whom the malignant spirits were after and if they had to burn down the house to get her – so be it!

The long-suffering Daniel Teed had reached the end of his willingness to lose sleep. In true Victorian melodrama fashion he pointed at the door and ordered the benighted Esther to leave and never agitate his poltergeist again. For some reason he overlooked Jennie's part in the haunting. Cut adrift by her family, alone in a sub-zero world, Esther was lucky to be taken in by a local restauranteur.

John White ran a small family restaurant and at first welcomed an extra pair of hands. The restaurant wasn't exactly throbbing with gourmets but sometimes a family of four might drop in for a Sunday roast and a gawk at his new acquisition. The expected rush of business didn't happen. Mr.White gave her $10 and a short goodbye.

Esther then moved from the position of being a phenomenon to that of a subject for scientific study. A sort of posh way of playing doctors and nurses without actually having to get your kit off in the sub-zero temperatures. Nothing happened. Any sounds rending the cold night air could not be interpreted as supernatural. After a while a wannabe scientist, James Beck, gave up the midnight vigils and showed poor Esther how the front door worked and suggested she

used her newly acquired technique. Daniel Teed got to hear about her new status as just another twenty-year-old and, nagged by his wife and Jennie, invited her back to share the family home. And it started all over again.

Enter, to a ripple of applause and a roll on the drums, Walter Hubbell. A doctor and sometime magician, he could see a profit in a stage show with a real poltergeist in attendance. His problem was that the spirits that considered Esther their own property weren't willing to share her soul with a charlatan and bombarded him with knives, paper weights, the old sofa or two and nasty wiggly things that smelled horrible. Delighted with the response Hubbell took a theatre, got Esther a stage and waited for the usual fusillade of domestic appliances.

Nothing happened!

Understandably the audience were a bit miffed and demanded their money back. Teed, who had invested modestly in Hubbell's show, decided that it was the end and ordered both Esther and the non-magic magician from his house.

What happened after that is a mystery. There is a story that Hubbell took Esther to New York and staged seances. Esther had picked up enough newspaper cuttings by now to make Habbell's claims for her supernatural powers seem respectable. It wasn't a success; they parted and Esther finished up in a mental hospital. A second version goes that after they split up, her powers, or lack of control, whichever way you want to look at it, returned and she burned to death in a barn. What is certain is that Hubbell wrote a book, *The Great Amhurst Mystery*, in 1879 and claimed that he had received sworn testimony from the major players in the melodrama, Dr Carritte, John White, the Teeds and Captain James Beck, and they all maintained that every flying spud and spontaneous combustion was true.

Which makes the mould-setting *Exorcist* not so far-fetched as it at first seems. The bed in both cases seems germane to what happened later. The distorted body and the showers of uncontrollable bric-a-brac and vegetable matter is familiar to both the film and the fact. In the Cox case the vegetable was potato whereas Linda Blair did an ace line in projectile mushy peas. A priest stood in for the sorely tried Teed and the slightly ambivalent ending left an opening for a sequel.

Possession is, of course, a good old standby of fiction. Mostly the possessed are up to something diabolical and have funny haircuts, crazy eyes and are extremely rude to anyone either un- or sub-possessed. There are occasions when the spirit has a kindly nature and directs his cast-on personality to do something nice. If not nice, at least funny. Take Danny Kaye in the 40s film *Wonder Man*. He plays two parts, a nerdy academic and a raunchy nightclub singer – twins. Both have girlfriends.

Nerd has a long-skirted librarian and Singer has a long-standing understanding with a showgirl. Singer witnesses a murder and gets sent into the afterlife for his pains. For some reason his soul doesn't make it to home base and hangs around his old haunts trying to get his own back on those who have done the dirty on him. This means taking over Nerd's body, which causes traumas between the disparate girlfriends. Nerd tries to fight off his brother's spirit but it's a task with nil chance of success. Problems arise as the breakdown of the barriers between the soul of Nerd and that of Singer cause confusion all around. All ends well with Nerd gradually being brought up to running speed by his ebullient twin. In the end you get a singing nerd with an overload of self-confidence and a split personality where his girlfriends are concerned.

14
Highwayman

So grant him life, but reckon
That the grave which housed him
May not be empty now

Robert Graves *To Bring the Dead to Life*

HIGHWAYMEN COME HIGH up on the ghostly menu. Give them a road like a ribbon of moonlight over a moor and a tavern or two and you have all the makings of a good haunting. Of all the gentlemen of the road it is the Essex boy, Dick Turpin, who has captured the imagination. There's hardly a village in the south east of England that doesn't claim some sort of connection. Or between London and York. Luckily the route between the two cities could be interpreted in many ways so Turpin's escape route seems to have made many diversions. But he still managed to turn up in York in time for the races and "prove" that he hadn't done the dastardly robbery the day before. His marathon ride on the gallant Black Bess put him in the clear but broke the mare's heart. Turpin had everything going his way then he stupidly went and shot a cockerel belonging to a neighbour who already had an inkling that the man next door in the cocked hat and mask might be more than just an inveterate masked-ball goer. The neighbour blew the whistle on Dick and he paid for his cock-shooting at the end of a rope in York City. There are, of course, many historians who claim that it wasn't Dick who made the epic journey at all but a road agent of a lesser breed called Swift John Nevison 50 years earlier. But what do they know?

It was a romantic age and highwaymen were very high profile. There wasn't a route out of any city that didn't have its regular gentleman ready to lift a purse or skirt as a way of breaking the tedium of a long journey. They were also good for business in the pub. Most of them were drinkers and, in funds, were willing to splash it about a bit. The expression "Drinks are on me" was made for the likes of Dick Turpin. Innkeepers, as a breed, always go for the latest gimmick. Jukeboxes not having been invented yet, every barman worth his pint swore that they had a "gentleman" as a regular. Soon that gentleman became Dick Turpin and an industry was born. The book *Rockwood* by W.H. Aimsworth was penned, the poem *The Highwayman* was rhymed, pub signposts were painted and the script for *Carry on Dick* was synopsized. With a big seller like that how could Turpin just get his neck stretched and die? There had to be more – and there was.

Once Dick was safely buried in a lime pit it was safe to assume that he would go a-haunting. Highly peripatetic in life he became just a dizzying blur in death. Soon reports were coming in from all over England that he had been sighted. Turpin would have loved it. During life he fed on the stories that were being told about him. He gave the post-hanging stories a healthy kickstart when he was led out to the gallows and hanged on a crisp April morning in 1739. He was just 33 and fancied himself as a bit of a ladies' man. The ladies fancied him as well so there was a good turn out for his send off. He rose magnificently to the occasion, saluted the crowd like a triumphant matador, blew a kiss to the simpering ladies in the front row – and leaped from the platform. The crowd was so impressed that the Sheriff's men couldn't stop the body from being seized and carted away. This gave rise to stories that Dick was still alive. There were still old men 50 years later either claiming to be the highwayman or being the friend who had cut him down, restored him to rude health and nurtured him all those years ago. The chance that he might still be alive didn't stop stories of a shadowy figure hanging around Turpin's old haunts. Just a year later a fanciful barmaid claimed that Dick came to her in the night and forced himself on her. When the baby made an appearance nine months later she tried to pass it off as the fruit of her union with the phantom but, as it had a shock of red hair exactly like the innkeeper's, the poor girl found it hard to get her story accepted and was driven from her garret by the landlord's wife.

It's not just the ghost of Turpin himself that pops up all over the place. His victims also get a fair billing. There's the old lady at Alderton Hall in Loughton, Essex. Dick turned up at the kitchen door begging for food. The kind-hearted old dear let him in but, before she could cook him a bacon butty, he pulled out a knife and threatened to cut off her interesting bits if she didn't tell him where she hid her sparklers. She wasn't having any of that. She tried to escape and call one of the servants but Turpin was more nimble and hauled her back. She still held out against his blandishments and in exasperation he threw her in the fire and held her there until she told him what he wanted to know. The plucky old girl died of her injuries but Turpin collected the trinkets and beat it back to Epping Forest. This was a Turpin escapade that the

rogue highwayman didn't star in after death. It is the old woman who runs screaming through the house looking for her lost fortune. The fireplace where Turpin did the deed is bricked up now but it still radiates an air of evil.

When Dick wasn't torturing old women he was being beastly on Hounslow Heath. Before the heath shrank to little more than a traffic island there were many reports of a devilish figure in a swirling black cape and mounted on a black horse, charging along the road straight at the oncoming traffic. Back in the 50s, Dick Turpin's galloping apparition was even used as an excuse in an insurance claim when a motorist ran off the road and wrecked his car against a stone wall.

It was at a pub near here, the Swan Inn, that Turpin is said to have come up with a merry jape to outwit his pursuers. He had the local blacksmith put the shoes on his horse the wrong way round, to make the posse think he was coming when he went. This ruse has also been attributed to Llewelyn, the last king of Wales. It didn't do him a lot of good either. At least it seems certain that the ploy didn't do Turpin any good – why else would he hang around the Swan Inn for eternity otherwise?

Returning from a stint on the heath to his native Essex, Dick dropped in on a farmer in Edgware. It wasn't exactly a social call. The farmer had a reputation as a bit of a miser and it was rumoured that he kept huge sacks of gold in the farmhouse. Dick Turpin wasn't the man to pass up anything that might yield a profit so he broke in and put the burning question to the farmer: "Show me your money!" The demand is simple enough but not easy to obey when it means the rewards of a lifetime are going to end up being frittered away on booze and women. At least not if you aren't going to be invited to the party. The farmer came over all truculent and told Dick what he could do with his brace of flintlocks. Not the cleverest repartee to a man who believed that everyone was just dying to tell him what he wanted to

know. Hadn't the old girl at Alderton Hall also had an infusion of memory about the whereabouts of her valuables only seconds before fire had liberated her tongue? He tried the same tactic on the farmer – with the same result. Not just with the sudden willingness of the farmer to be cooperative with the location of his nest egg but also in liberating his spirit to loaf around on the astral plane making a nuisance of himself.

Just to show that Turpin wasn't parochial and limited to the profitable pickings on the outskirts of London he has a few of his favourite haunts in the Midlands. In every inn between London and the Scottish border that bears the name of Dick Turpin, you will find a plethora of the psychically inclined ready and willing to swear that Dandy Dick has come on strong to them. And when he's not seen there are the ghostly hoof-beats. Even places that have no direct contact with him have heard the thunder of Black Bess's hooves and the shrieks and sighs of assorted maidens that have come within the Highwayman's grasp.

Most spectacular is Turpin's *pièce de resistance* in Epping Forest, just a pistol shot away from the Dick Turpin roundabout and public house. There, on a still moonlit night, the shade of Turpin gallops through the trees, dragging, hanging from his saddle, a woman in a white shift. It is said that she is the daughter of an innkeeper who tried to sell him to the local JP. Unfortunately for her the JP was a friend of Dick's and warned him that the constables were coming to get him. Turpin didn't like that sort of thing so he took the landlord's daughter, tied her hands to his saddle and dragged her through the forest until she was dead.

A macabre little story from near where the concrete cows of Milton Keynes stand now is a touching tale of a father and daughter. The daughter had the hots for a highwayman and, whenever she thought her father wasn't looking, enticed him into her bedroom for a bit of highly exciting but dangerous nooky. Of course, Dad had to spoil it. He came back early from a night out with the boys and the highwayman – let us suppose that it was Dick Turpin – was only saved from being caught *in flagrante* by the quick-witted, but doomed, girl. She pushed him into a cupboard and then, instead of jumping into bed and pretending to be asleep in the true tradition of bedroom farce, followed her lover in and shut the door. Her parent wasn't fooled. To teach them a lesson he barricaded the door with the heavy bedroom furniture and left them in there. He obviously had a lot of bile preserving his hatred because when at last he opened the cupboard door the girl was dead and Turpin had only just enough strength to get to his horse and ride away.

In 1940 an evacuee, Doreen Price, was boarded in the house and slept in the fateful room. She claimed that on many occasions when she was in bed she heard sobs and cries from the corner where the cupboard used to be. On a couple of occasions she even saw the ghostly form of a woman, with hands outstretched as if pleading with her for help. Since then there have been many sightings – or hearings – from the room. It has become a bit of a mecca for ghosthunters with time on their hands and a couple of gallons in the tank to shoot up the M1 and listen for the anguished cries and the sounds of Dick's horse, galloping off through the night.

Dick isn't scared of the modern world. Heathrow airport stands on part of what Turpin considered his western manor when things got too hot for him in Essex. His ghost still haunts the halls and corridors but it appears he has given up his horse and now breezes around touching up simpering lady passengers and making suggestive grunting noises when there's a lovely stewardess around. How they know it's phantom Dick is a bit of a mystery. Then again, it might as well be him as anybody else. Perhaps he will wander aboard a Jumbo heading west one day and will link up with the ghost of Jack the Ripper on London Bridge over Lake Havasu.

15
Equipment

Ha! while I gaze, pale Cynthia fades,
The bursting Earth unveils the Shades!
All slow, and wan, and wrap'd with Shrouds,
They rise in visionary Crowds,
And all with sober Accent cry,
"Think, Mortal, what it is to dye."

Thomas Parnell *A Night Piece on Death*

MODERN GHOSTS ARE very technology minded. There have been reports that they have used telephones to get in touch with friends and family left behind. Hopefully getting a good deal from BT's "Friends & Family" offer. A phantom beat several shades of hell out of a Baltimore typewriter a few years ago. The message that came over was garbled but someone actually made a sort of sense out of it and confirmed that the writer was trying to get in touch with someone. Specifically who was hard to decide. Probably worried about the fact they hadn't finished their typing course and were trying to see if there was a refund on offer. As technology advances so does the means of communication. I'm sure somebody already has had a one-to-one on the Internet. In fact if you're surfing you come across a lot of information that appears to come from another dimension.

The increased use of the latest technology by those who have gone over has been reciprocated by the ghostbusters. At one time it was left to the psychic, a sensitive who could walk into a house with a problem, sniff out the cause of the problem and, with a few deft incantations and a whiff of incense, lay the disturbed spirit to rest. No longer! Now the poor ghostbuster has to come prepared for all the modern tricks ghosts get up to on the astral plane.

One of the main weapons that the investigators use is a camera. Not just any old camera. Ghosts have proved notoriously shy over the last century. There was a time when anybody with a Brownie box camera and a role of sensitive film could practically guarantee to come up with a disturbing picture. A curious, indistinct figure in a window a couple of hundred yards away. A shaft of light on a stairway where no light had been seen before. A disembodied head floating in the background seemed to come in the box with the film. It took the apparitions, who had carelessly let themselves be committed to emulsion, a few years to get the hang of it but once they had learned the trick with the camera shutter it became increasingly hard to capture their image. What could the ghostbusters do, poor things? After sitting up all night, freezing their boleros off, and then having nothing to show the rest of the gang down at the Ghost Club must have been very demoralising. Then someone came up with the answer. Infra red. Infra-red cameras ignore the ultra-violet range and hone in on the lower range. What they photograph, in effect, is heat. It is a good try but ghosts are chuckling merrily away all over limbo. They know that when they are about everyone complains of the cold. There doesn't seem to be many photographs of ghosts picked out from their surroundings in a leprous red so far. Other cameras are used as well. And Polaroid. Polaroid is very good. So far there hasn't been what everyone has agreed is a Polaroid snapshot of a photogenic apparition yet but all the experts agree that when they do get a picture it is going to be on a Polaroid camera.

Ghosts are sometimes very noisy. It is therefore necessary to have sound-recording equipment. The human ear takes in a very restricted range, 20cps to 20kcps, for those with normal hearing. This sort of terrestrial restriction does not apply to ghosts. Okay, so they are into a bit of table rapping and shoe shuffling but the really interesting sounds are to be found at a much higher range. Equipment has been specially adapted to take in these higher reaches. Now the top pros in the ghostbusting business have microphones that can hear a pin drop at 30 feet and the sound of wind through the veins of a feather as it falls in a darkened room. This can lead to some amusing and embarrassing eavesdropping if it's been a quiet night and the group is mixed. So far the expensive and highly sensitive apparatus has picked up all sorts of noises, some at frequencies that would have a dog howling like a loon. Unfortunately no indisputable message has been received but, again, the experts are positive that when the call comes it will be above the hearing range of us poor mortals.

Another indispensable piece of equipment is the thermometer. Thermometers come in a wide range of shapes and sizes, from long slender instruments to be inserted in various unmentionable orifices to big butch machines to measure the temperature inside a nuclear furnace. It is notoriously difficult to not only get near enough to insert a thermometer in a ghost, it is almost impossible to find an orifice capable of accommodating a thermometer. An instrument has been devised that just sits around in a site that will hopefully be used by a visiting spirit and detect any unaccountable change in temperature. This can also be linked to the cameras. A fairly useless operation as the recorded temperature is usually lower than normal.

Tremblers of acute and varying sensitivity are another must. These can be linked through the camera and sound equipment so that a passing truck can set off a barrage of flashing lights and whirring tapes. All these have to be analysed back at base when the excitement of the hunt has died down.

All is not high-tech in the ghostbusters' world although if you happen to see the facetious film of the same name you might be forgiven for thinking it is. Dan Akroyd and his crew have these dirty great vacuum-cleaner things that they direct at anything that doesn't seem of this dimension and somehow, using the tractor beam originated by Captain James Kirk on the Star Ship Enterprise, immobilises the oddball creatures and traps them in the bag of their psychic Hoover. Ridiculous, of course. And I'm not too happy about the ghosts that the busters bust. These usually appear to be composed of green slime or something equally offensive. Another reason for doubting the veracity of the creatures is that they seem to hang out in peculiar places. Would you expect to find an authentic representative of the spirit world hanging out in a refrigerator?

The roots of the discipline are still preserved by modern ghosthunters. Pens, notebook, tape measures, talcum powder, cotton thread, trip wire, labels, mirrors, thumbtacks, luminous paint and, of course, a reliable watch that can be easily synchronised. What are they all for? It is not really apparent at first glance but when you think about it the mystery is easily cleared up. Obviously the pen and notebook go together. And the watch. A mysterious bump in the night and everyone checks their Accurist. Next morning they compare times and check the accuracy of the manufacturer's claim. If the tremblers and sensitive sound recorders have done their job and time recorded it, the notebook does become a little superfluous to requirements but, in the ghostbusting world, it's better to be safe than passed over. The tape measures are of prime importance. As soon as the flash light flashes two members of the team leap into action and start measuring. Although it is a function germane to the very heart of a ghosthunter's activity no-one has yet found out exactly what to measure and what the measurements can be used for. Fortunately a lot of research is being done on this aspect of the researchers' routine and an announcement is expected any minute. It will probably be found that it has a lot to do with the talcum powder. This is not used, as you might suppose, to ease the bottoms of the ghostbusters sitting around all night, not daring to move to find a more comfortable position in case they set off the equipment. It is used to sort out the psychic footprints from those of any prankster who might think it funny to upset the results of the watcher. What sort of footprint a ghost might make is open to speculation.

Cotton thread and trip wires are part and parcel with the talcum powder. Ghosts, unless very pranksome, do not go around leaving imprints in the powder, breaking strategically placed threads and blundering into trip wires. Ghostbusters are very responsible investigators and do not like their meticulously recorded outings held up to ridicule by other, less committed, thrill seekers. A

little book of labels is always handy. Not least for tagging any of the footsteps in the talcum powder that might not be considered kosher. If there does seem to be a chance that there is someone less serious, thumbtacks can be spread around the area of the talcum powder. The leading ghostbuster suggests that, to obviate the chance of a random noise upsetting any shy spook from putting in an appearance, everyone should take off their shoes. This may also create an ambience that the ghost finds more amenable – on the other hand it mightn't. Mirrors are important for morale. What can be more upsetting than to spend a night in a draughty, abandoned mansion house, look a wreck in the morning and not have a mirror to confirm your state of dissemble. The really devilish wheeze is the luminous paint. This is by way of being a morale booster. If there are unaccountable forms moving around in the dark and it's essential to pinpoint the marauder you can splash on some luminous paint and everyone can report having seen a luminous shape, moving in a disembodied manner, blundering into tripwires, creating footprints, hopping around on thumbtacks and testing out the efficacy of the ghostbusters' equipment.

One of the problems of ghostly encounters is what the boys in blue down at the local nick might call phantom forensics. That little dollop of ectoplasm that the pathologist can run under his microscope or the smudged ethereal dab that a fingerprint expert could search for the mandatory 16 whorls. There is also the believability factor. Questions that remain unanswered. Like, when a ghost pops back to haunt someone, why is he wearing clothes? Surely material that is, as far as most people are concerned, dead. If someone dies a violent death, which is the kicking off point for most hauntings, surely he or she doesn't need to be stuck with the gear they chucked on that morning with no intimation that this was going to be their costume for all

eternity. Unless this is an indication that ghosts are really creatures from hell. Maybe most men would be happy to wait patiently in T-shirt and jeans for kingdom to come and be risen from the dead, in line for a new outfit. Most women wouldn't. Even if you were run over by the winner at Ascot shortly after you had been singled out by TV cameras as the most stunningly dressed woman in the paddock, by the following Saturday you would be in despair that you were welded to an outrageously stupid Shilling hat and a dress that was already *démodé*.

Another question that bugs anyone seriously thinking about the haunting fraternity is – what do they, the ghosts, think about all this haunting? There they are, presumably out of time and space, with nothing concrete to do but skulk about making a nuisance of themselves and none of their peers to appreciate their talent or give them advice. Or maybe they have ghostly bull-baiting sessions. Maybe every Walpurgis Night, after a couple of hours of concentrated spooking, they all get together for a rave. It would account for the odd idea that the skies are alive with flying witches that night. It might also account for a few UFOs as well.

Whenever we hear about hauntings it is, *per force*, from the haunted's point of view. What we need, to get a sense of perspective, is an insight into how the haunter looks at its role in life/death. How do spectres manage their time? Do they have the same timespan as those left behind? Does the Accurist work in the afterlife? If it does, what happens if it goes wrong? And do ghosts use calenders? One of the chief characteristics of a ghost seems to be the ability to accurately gauge the passing of years. Every ghostbuster worth his go at the ectoplasm knows of ancestral visitors who appear punctually at some important point in the year. "It's the second Sunday after Epiphany so I'd better waft down to the Grange and give that lot a good seeing to." Is that the sort of thing that flashes through the spooky synapses once a year? And what was agitating the defunct molecules in between haunting appointments? Just what did happen when the Julian calender changed to Gregorian? Did the ghostly thereafter have the same sort of panic as the real world gets when the summer time thing needs changing?

These matters aside, there is the broader aspect. Assume that the more astute ghosts know what's what. At certain times and in conditions peculiar to their own fancy, they have to appear, visually, aurally or noisomely, at a place designated by the circumstances of their demise. How does he see it? Does he find it a chore or a bit of a giggle in an otherwise boring non-existence? Is the phantom aware that it has passed over the great divide? Does it sleep and count the passing of days by the activity of the sun and moon? Or is there some sort of angelic town crier who whips around stirring the more reluctant haunt specialist into activity.

Maybe the whole idea that a ghost is aware that it is a ghost needs some investigation. Could it be that when a person dies they carry on unaware that they have passed into the spirit world because it isn't another land that they enter but just another time? Let's look at the sordid story of the venal Count Roger de Palfrey.

16
Palfrey's Bane

Thy bones are marrowless, thy blood is cold;
Thou hast no speculation in those eyes
Which thou dost glare with.

William Shakespeare *Macbeth*

COUNT ROGER DE PALFREY coughed and spat with precision onto the flaring end of one of the logs. His head ached and his eyeballs throbbed under lids like scalding cups. He had given up trying to work out whether his discomfort was due to sitting in the corner of the draughty open fireplace or to the deteriorating, and fast-disappearing quality of the wine in his cellar.

Briefly he though of going back to the cellar.

It was his favourite haunt. There he could sit amongst the empty, decayed shelves and collapsed barrels and drink himself into a stupor that blotted out all the recent ugliness. The thought of the cellar attracted him but the dense, soporific smoke had robbed him of the will to do anything. He pulled the smelly blanket of raddled furs closer and tried to find some comfort on the wooden bench for his flabby buttocks. Tears, partly from the wood smoke but mostly from his well of self-pity, trickled down his cheeks, making a pink stream through the collected grime.

"It's not fair!" he sobbed to himself and spat into the fireplace again as a magic seal to mark the enmity of the fates. The smoking fire cast sluggish shadows on the damp stone walls and highlighted the drab, rotting tapestries.

The obvious poverty of the surroundings was so all-enveloping that it was impossible to imagine the bare, comfortless castle as ever being different. But Roger could remember! When he was in his cups his favourite refuge was in the years before the war. The bright sunny years before his father had put a black mark on the family escutcheon that had never been removed. Palfrey senior's fall from grace by backing the wrong pretender to the throne could have been expiated when the whim of fortune changed later and promoted to power a more sympathetic clique, but by that time the old man was dead and Roger had squandered what little money was left on further inappropriate liaisons.

Twenty years had passed since the Palfrey name had meant anything at any court, no matter how temporarily or degraded. In all that time the only slight hiatus in Palfrey's slide down the greasy bannister to obscurity had occurred when he had married Essodena. Her family were new to the aristocracy. Her father, now the Duc de Parange and close to the throne, had started life as the seventh son of a minor squire in the barbarous eastern forests. Roger's father, a knight of the old lineage, had held the Duc's grandfather as a vassal in the old days. The Duc hadn't realised how far the Palfrey family had fallen when Roger offered to take his eldest daughter off his hands. It seemed like a good marriage. The future Duc had consolidated his family's claim to autonomy in the east and was looking for more universal honours. He didn't get them through Roger, who promised much and delivered nothing. Parange got tired of kicking his heels waiting to be called to court. He assembled his considerable army and six weeks later was pounding on Roger de Palfrey's drawbridge.

What he saw he didn't like.

Only the weight of the ponderous stones and the skill of the stonemasons in dry-joint building stopped the castle collapsing in on itself. Many of the minor buildings had already succumbed and there wasn't a stable where any self-respecting groom would bed down a horse.

Essodena had always been a shrew. It was one of the reasons the Duc hadn't pried too closely into de Palfrey's coffers when he had offered to take her away and make a countess out of her. Her temper hadn't improved since finding herself the mistress of a comfortless ruin and a vicious, drunken husband. But her father was still only a common landlord with some uncommitted military muscle at that time. De Palfrey had whined to him about his hardship and offered to give Essodena back to him. The offer sent a cold shiver through Parange. Grudgingly he gave de Palfrey a purse of silver and hastily left for the capital before the subject of his daughter's future welfare could be broached again. Since then the country squire had become a powerful aristocrat and, as the Duc de Parange, a constant jogger of regal elbows.

De Palfrey's frequent attempts to capitalise on his father-in-law's good fortune had met with constant rebuff. The Duc was aware that the only chance of a return to favour open to de Palfrey was a lavish display of wealth. A chance that the Duc de Parange had no intention of financing.

Roger was a well-used thirty-five-year-old. When he wasn't drinking and went to the trouble of cleaning himself up he was still presentable, in a dilapidated way. He hardly ever saw Essodena. She had gathered together the last of the usable furnishings and isolated herself in a couple of rooms in a less spartan part of the castle. There she lived a pious existence along with an expelled nun from a local nunnery.

On one of Roger's rare journeys to the nearest town of Bersaler he had received an offer that appealed to him. An offer that did not include his sanctimonious wife. Every once in a while he would surface above the constant level of alcohol fumes, take a look at his surroundings and decide to do something about it. The furthest his determination went was to the house of Ingo Lombard, who already held papers on all the land and property that came with the overlordship of the castle, and try and wheedle an extension of his already moribund mortgage. Lombard's usual attitude was such that Palfrey would return home to ward off the incipient frostbite with a few bottles of the more toxic remains of his cellar. This time his reception at the Lombard villa had been different.

The old usurer had loaned him a little gold and asked him to stay to dinner. Food was almost a novelty to de Palfrey's stomach and was as heady as the wine. Later in the evening Lombard had produced his daughter, Lubina. She was a knockout and even de Palfrey, through his alcoholic lenses, found himself smitten. Lombard was so anxious that de Palfrey should be favourably disposed towards his daughter that he got the wrong end of the stick. When his amorous advances had been rejected and a couple of the Lombard retainers were sitting on his chest to make sure that the old man had his full attention, he was told that Lubina was available for marriage – and nothing else.

Ingo Lombard did sweeten the pill slightly by intimating that he wouldn't be upset if he could incorporate the sign of the three golden balls into de Palfrey's more traditional devices on his coat of arms.

Roger just managed to stop himself giving a long-winded explanation of his marital status. It seemed unlikely that the well-informed banker had overlooked this unfortunate liaison. Especially as Essodena was the daughter of the now powerful Duc de Parange.

De Palfrey needed time to think.

He carefully bid Lombard goodbye leaving open the subject of their future relationship until he had managed to unpickle his brain cells long enough to evaluate the new intelligence. The process had been painful.

That was why he was sitting in the corner of the fireplace instead of in the cellar within arm's-length of alcoholic oblivion. What was needed was obvious.

He had to get rid of Essodena!

With his wife gone he would have the run of Lubina's beautiful body and, what was more important, his new father-in-law would move into the castle and pay for the privilege. The stupid Essodena was the problem!

Pious she might be but a countess she intended to remain. Without her compliance it would be impossible to better his fortune by welcoming the Lombards into the family. But how could he get rid of Essodena?

The question thudded at him constantly. Any move that might upset her would bring a squad of marriage guidance counsellors from her father. Roger shuddered to think of the greetings they would bring. The Duc was not going to have his daughter humiliated whatever happened. And he definitely wasn't going to take her back into his own household.

Essodena had to disappear! It was the "how" that was driving de Palfrey to the breaking point. He was just drifting away in a smoke-drugged sleep when he heard the door yawn open on rusty hinges and the pad of feet directed towards him. He closed his eyes and pretended to sleep. Whoever it was they were going to be complaining. One of the two remaining serfs whining about not having any food or the nun sent by his wife to make some chauvinistic demand.

The slap of leather sandals stopped a few feet away and he peered through the gloom under lowered lashes. It was one of the servants. Roger groaned to himself. He wished he could sustain the energy to whip the staff regularly so that they would keep their complaints to themselves if they valued a whole hide.

"There's someone to see you," the man said with no attempt at civility in his voice. Roger felt the clutch of fear. The only people that ever came to the castle were usually there for blood.

His blood!

So far he had managed to keep his eight pints untapped but he didn't like anything to happen that might threaten his vital reservoir.

"Who is it?" he asked, shrinking back into the corner and pulling his blanket high up around his ears so that only his red-rimmed eyes and thinning hair could be seen above it. Having delivered his message the servant turned away and made for the door and the warmth of the kitchen. Roger shouted his question again. The man waited until he got to the door before answering.

"A messenger from the Duc de Parange," he replied grudgingly and went out, slamming the door behind him. The messenger from his father-in-law could mean anything. It might even mean that the old man had shuffled off this mortal coil and left everything to his beloved daughter. De Palfrey didn't dwell much on that possibility. It was more likely he was being sent a reprimand. A veiled, or not so veiled, threat that if he didn't shape up and live up to his newly elevated in-laws' place in society he could expect a painful visitation.

With an effort Roger pulled himself together. He tried to do something about his clothing but it hadn't been off his body in months and was nailed in place by sweat and the rancid human smell made piquant by stale wine. As he hurried to the reception hall he hoped that Essodena hadn't heard the visitor arrive. He wanted to find out what he was in for before the harridan appeared and wrought humiliating confusion.

The man waiting for him was impressive. Above average height, with a silk chasuble over his gleaming armour. Roger tried not to betray his envy of the bright, well-oiled breastplate with its exaggerated custom-built contours. The helmet was also in the latest carbonated iron that made it so lightweight and malleable.

Roger surmounted his feeling of inferiority by assuring himself that it was all a bit gauche and *nouveau riche* and not at all the attire of a true gentleman. The soldier made himself known. He was the captain of one of the Duc de Parange's squads. He made no pretence of the way he felt about de Palfrey and curtly told him that he had come to take the Countess Essodena to the Duc's palace.

Hopefully de Palfrey asked the reason. He was deflated when the captain told him that the Duc was only complying with a request from his daughter and expected her to return to her husband within the month.

Roger was annoyed by his manner but knew better than to provoke a confrontation. Especially as he suspected that the captain was spoiling for a fight and could expect only approbation from the old Duc if he was able to report that he had dished out a salutary lesson to the impoverished Count.

Tension was released by the arrival of Essodena trailed by her wayward nun who swayed more than the cruel draughts in the hall warranted. Roger eyed her suspiciously. He suspected the nun of being a contributing factor to his cellar running dry although he had never caught her bottle-handed. Essodena was ready to leave but the captain persuaded her it would be better to stay overnight and catch the dawn light.

Roger hung around hopefully. He wasn't fond of his father-in-law but he would happily forget that for a chance of the food and wine that always loaded the Parange table. Essodena and the captain made it very plain that Count de Palfrey was not one of the noblesse who were being obliged.

All evening de Palfrey sulked in the cellar. The more he drank the more determined he became that he was going to solve his problem. Somehow he was going to get rid of the dead weight of a shrewish wife with miserly, though dangerous, relatives. He let his mind wander around the alternatives that would clear the ground for a fruitful relationship with Lombard and his luscious daughter, Lubina.

Unbidden his thought settled on Death!

The more he thought about it the more obvious it seemed. It wasn't a new idea: many a pleasant alcohol-fortified dream had been enhanced by the imagined feel of his wife's scrawny neck between his hands.

In the slough of depression the following morning he had thought more of the retribution his prickly father-in-law would exact.

But ...!

What if he could do away with her and divert suspicion elsewhere? After all, the Duc had sent a picked guard for her. How could the powerless Count Roger de Palfrey be blamed if they mysteriously disappeared in the forest after leaving his castle? Excited by the prospect he planned how it could be carried out. There was only one time when it would be possible.

That night!

The four-man escort had settled into the kitchen. Roger, originally, had no intention of being hospitable but now he felt it could help his plan if he supplied them with a few flagons of wine from his meagre stock. If he decided not to go through with what he planned all he had lost was some inferior wine. The captain was another problem! He was busy being the ladies' man for the Countess Essodena and her nun friend.

Roger smiled as he thought of the secret trap in the stone floor of the cellar. The trap door covered a disused seige well. A couple of years earlier the wooden frames holding the doors had collapsed and Roger had jammed a couple of makeshift wedges in the sides to hold them until he got around to fixing the trap properly.

He never had!

The more he thought about it the more feasible it became. The heavy wine he drank constantly kept his nerve steady and rose-tinted any cracks in his master stratagem. For Essodena he reserved something special. He smiled happily to himself as he thought of the pleasure he would get in stilling his wife's strident voice once and for always!

Having set the escort on the road to alcoholic oblivion and eased the wooden pegs on the trapdoor so that any extra weight would force it open, he sat in the corner of the cellar and thought about the change in fortune his marriage to Lubina Lombard would bring. He was careful not to drink too much – just enough to keep his nerve steady and his brain divorced from too much reality. When he could no longer stay awake and risked wrecking his shaky plan by dropping off to sleep, he decided it was time to act. With exaggerated caution he crept to the dark, lofty room that used to be the armoury. There he found, amongst the rusty remnants of his family's martial past, a double handed battle axe. The blade was badly pitted with rust and the wooden handle had all but disintegrated, but Palfrey wasn't expecting to have to fight with it – just lop off a head or two. The short sword he intended to use for the main work of the night was in better condition. It was the one he occasionally wore if he ventured out of the castle. It wasn't in prime condition either but he kept the blade relatively sharp and used it for a variety of daily jobs for which the noble tine had not been intended. Frightened that his resolve wouldn't last he went swiftly to the kitchen and looked in.

Essodena's escorts were all asleep. Regarding de Palfrey as nothing more than a weak drunken fool they had discarded their armour and were now sprawled around the dying fire in a heavy, wine-induced sleep. Roger eyed the recumbent figures and felt fear weaken his resolve. It wasn't going to be easy to dispatch the four fighting men even if they were asleep. One was lying along the settle in the fireplace, his head resting on his arm. He was one for the knife. Another sat on the wooden bench beside the table, his head resting on his hands in front of him. Roger eyed his unguarded neck. A possible axe victim! The third was in the heavy wooden chair on the far side of the fireplace, a leg hitched over the arm and his head resting on his fist. He was obviously not too comfortable. Even as Count de Palfrey watched, the big man moaned and creakily resettled his heavy body in a momentarily easier position.

Roger couldn't make up his mind whether he was a candidate for axe or sword. For a moment he couldn't see the fourth man and panic hit him. He spun round and looked fearfully along the corridor expecting the last guard to appear behind him. Seeing nothing he calmed himself and eased around the door. The fourth man was lying stretched out in a cot he had fashioned for himself out of de Palfrey's fur cloak and bits and pieces he had gleaned from the other rooms of the castle. He would be number one for the knife.

Roger crept around the supine form and knelt down at its head. A quick glance at the others reassured him. De Palfrey took a deep breath, clamped his hand over the doomed man's mouth and drove his sword savagely into his neck. The man heaved upwards, his feet kicking wildly but muffled by the soft couch he had made himself. In panic de Palfrey bore down on the sword practically severing his victim's neck before the man slumped and was still.

A wild terror seized de Palfrey as he contemplated his

handiwork. Until that moment his plan had been like a dream – easily confused with his drunken reveries in the cellar. The spreading blood and the ghastly wound in front of him jolted him into stark reality. Now, unless he was able to carry through his ill-conceived plan, he would be cut to pieces by his victim's companions. And Essodena would have the last laugh!

The thought of Essodena's triumph steadied him. Who would be his next victim? He discounted the man at the table. It would be impossible to kill him without waking the others. The restless man in the chair? He represented the greatest menace. De Palfrey slid noiselessly across the floor. Once more his sword flashed and the carmined point sunk into the soldier's throat. Roger held the man upright in the chair until consciousness had fled. Still the remaining two were unaware of their danger.

Sweating, fighting nausea provoked not by the horrendous deed he was committing but by fear that he might yet be foiled, he crept across to the man in the settle. It was not going to be easy to dispatch him without risking waking the man at the table. The settle, situated well back in the open fireplace, made it impossible to get close to him before attempting the fatal thrust with the blade. Using the axe was likely to be noisy. Anyway, the low chimney breast restricted anything but an underhand blow and the man wasn't sitting in a position for that to be effective. Nervously Palfrey looked at the man asleep at the table, torn between the expanse of pink unprotected neck and the risk of waking the hard-looking warrior in the settle before he was ready for him.

Fear made the decision for him.

The man on the settle shifted and smacked his lips like a baby. In panic de Palfrey raised his sword to chest height. As he hesitated the soldier's eyes opened. He blinked, not appreciating his danger at first. As his perilous position became obvious to him and his hand darted for his sword, de Palfrey lunged forward.

Too late, the doomed man tried to get to his feet, his sword half out of its scabbard. The murderer's sword bit deeply into his neck, severing his windpipe and spinal column in one blow. As he collapsed sideways his twitching nerves completed the withdrawal of his sword and it flew across the kitchen to land with a clatter almost at the feet of the remaining member of Essodena's escort. With an oath he stumbled to his feet, the heavy chair crashing back on the flagstones. With a practised draw his sword was in his hand, sleep banished by the danger-produced adrenalin. Under normal circumstances he would have been more than a match for the profligate Count but de Palfrey was in a world of his own. Terror had robbed him of all thought. Just the maniacal desire to finish his macabre mission as quickly as possible remained. With a banshee scream he hurled his dripping sword across the kitchen. The soldier deflected it with the blade of his own sword but before he could recover a guard position de Palfrey threw himself forward directing all his weight and fury into the arm holding the heavy battle-axe. The attacked man almost recovered in time but his slanted blade was swept aside and the axe-head thudded into his chest, cutting through his ribs and dissecting his heart. As he fell to the ground de Palfrey stood over him hacking and cutting until his arms could no longer lift the axe. He staggered back and sunk down against the wall. As the blood of his four victims laced lines along the flagstone joints and fused together in a colourful, widening pool, de Palfrey fought his weakening resolve to finish the job. All he wanted to do was rush out into the night, away from the grizzly scene he had painted.

Reason prevailed. He was too far along the path to step aside now! Once the dead men were discovered a search would begin for the perpetrator of the crime. And nothing would stop the Duc's men until they had found him and subjected him to the most painful death their fertile imaginations could conjure up.

Count de Palfrey pushed himself to his feet and, avoiding the accusing cadavers, slowly left the kitchen. Now began the most dangerous part of his plan. He took a rush torch from the wall and started towards the west turret where the escort captain was sleeping. In the guttering light he noticed the state of his clothes. Blood soaked him from head to foot and for a moment he thought of going to his room to change. Then a sly smile creased his face, but did not enter his eyes. What better camouflage than to present himself to the captain as the victim of an attack?

Quickly, before his nerve failed him, he ripped his clothes and made sure that his face was literally tinted with the blood of his victims. Outside the captain's door he extinguished the light. Without knocking he burst in and, with a cry, sank to his knees. A torch fluttered on the wall opposite the bed. It was enough for the captain to appreciate the apparition of horror crouching just inside the door. With an oath he leaped from his bed and picked up his sword. De Palfrey had to be careful now. He wanted to keep the captain on the move and didn't want him to have a chance to examine what was going on too closely. With a pathetic cry and a palsied, pointing finger, de Palfrey staggered to his feet and led the way out of the chamber. The pad of bare feet behind him and the string of breathless questions told him that his ruse was working. De Palfrey gambled on the captain not being too familiar with the house and being willing to follow his nightmare guide.

Even when he led the way to the cellar! As they entered the cellar, the captain had second thoughts. The run had winded him and he wanted a rest. Grabbing de Palfrey by the shoulder he slammed him against the wall.

But it was already too late!

De Palfrey screamed and looked with fear-crazed eyes behind the panting captain. His act was so good that, thinking he was about to be attacked, the captain spun round to face the imagined attacker and stepped onto the loosened boards of the seige well. As the trap canted downwards the soldier threw himself sideways and managed to cling to the side of the well. His scrabbling feet couldn't find purchase on the slimy walls.

"Help me!" he appealed to de Palfrey.

Count Roger walked slowly across to the well side and looked down on the struggling man, a satisfied smile on his lips. Without a word he stamped down on the clinging fingertips and then leaned forward with interest to watch his last victim plummet down into the icy waters below. He sat beside the well until the sounds beneath him had ceased and then stood up. Now the hardest but the most pleasurable part of the operation began!

In his wife's room he found her asleep, her arms around the ex-nun, deep in the nest of blankets and furs she had stripped from the rest of the castle. De Palfrey didn't waste time! Ignoring the nun he took his wife by the hair and dragged her screaming from her couch. Her companion tried to save her but was felled by a savage blow from de Palfrey. In the cellar Count Roger had already positioned the heavy chair, which he usually sat in to sample his bottles, in a small alcove behind one of the buttresses holding up the heavy ceiling and the even heavier castle above. With a few deft twists he tied her securely to the chair and then slapped her viciously across the face to stop her screaming.

"I'm going to leave you for a little while, my dear. I have a few chores to do first and then it will be just the two of us." He patted his stunned wife's cheek and stepped back.

"Have a look at this while I'm gone," he suggested, indicating the building blocks piled at the side of the alcove. They had been put there a long time ago when there had been talk of extending the cellar. At last a use had been found for them. De Palfrey nodded contentedly. "I'm going to make you a retreat where you won't be disturbed by anyone. Not me, not your friend, not the captain – not even your loving father!"

Before Essodena could say anything he turned on his heel and left. The nun was just coming around when he got to her. Casually he punched her behind the ear and then picked her up and took her down to the cellar. As he got near he could hear the shrill, desperate screams of his wife. It was like music to his ears and he smiled happily to himself. He showed Essodena the unconscious figure of her companion before he negligently tipped her down the well to join the captain. As he dragged the slaughtered escorts from the kitchen and dropped them to their watery but companionable grave he fancied Essodena's screams became louder and more gratifying.

Half a dozen buckets of water washed away the worst of the evidence in the kitchen and then he was ready for the last and most satisfying task. There were still four hours or so until daybreak and he didn't expect to have problems with his undisciplined servants for at least a couple of hours after. Ignoring Essodena's cries and entreaties he slowly manoeuvred the slabs of stone into place and calked them with a mortar mixture that had also lain around for a good many years.

In the early dawn he stepped back and looked at his handiwork. It wasn't likely to get him contracts to build castles for his allies but would have recommended him strongly to the enemy. The thick wall effectively cut off the doomed woman's cries. De Palfrey stood for a few moments with his ear pressed to the wall. He was a little disappointed to be able to hear nothing.

He was still dreaming happily when he was jerked out of his sleep by a long, wailing, soul-piercing scream. The sweat poured down him as he sat on the edge of the bed and tried to rationalise what he heard. How could it be his wife, now safely entombed beneath the castle? Surely she couldn't make so much noise that she could be heard this far away? There must be a flue or a diversion between the walls he assured himself and felt easier in his mind. When he went out into the corridor the shrill cacophony followed him. Panicking, he rushed through the corridors and down the stairs to the cellar. In his headlong flight he nearly shared the fate of the gallant captain and his men. Just in time he slithered to a halt and gingerly picked his way around the gaping hole of the seige well.

The noise in the cellar was no greater than in his bedroom but he pressed his ear against the wall to be as near to the source of the sound as possible. With futile anger he beat on the stone and shouted at his wife to be quiet. He felt it was most inconsiderate of her to plague him in such an uncouth manner.

Suddenly he thought of the servants. He still thought of the old man and woman who grudgingly provided the odd meal for him as servants. What if they heard the screams and decided to report them to the Duc de Parange when he inevitably sent another party to find out what had happened. With a stream of abuse inadequately trying to drown out the more effective vocalisation of his victim, Count de Palfrey ran to the kitchen. The scene inside was so normal he skidded to a halt in the doorway in surprise. The old man was crouched down by the fire putting on a couple of logs to try and combat the refrigerated chill of the bare stones while his wife stood at the table stripping the skin off a rabbit. They both looked up in dull surprise at the Count leaning against the door jam, panting for breath, his eyes rolling maniacally, dirt plastered thickly in his hair and covering his torn tunic. He didn't look much different from usual. The drink would carry him off before long and then they would pick up what they could and move on. They both turned back to their tasks.

De Palfrey didn't know quite what to do. They acted as if they couldn't hear the wild screams echoing through the kitchen. Obviously they were playing a game. Pretending they didn't know what he had done so that they would be able to sell him to his father-in-law when the time came.

He couldn't have that!

Lurching forward he tried to grab the old woman. Deftly she stepped to one side and hit him in the face with the bloodied carcass in her hand. De Palfrey fell across the table. In front of him was a sharp knife. Quickly he grabbed it and turned towards the woman who stood watching him, the dismembered rabbit swinging in her hand ready to repel any attack. De Palfrey walked slowly towards her, the knife held menacingly at waist level. He had forgotten the old man by the fireplace. A blow across the back of the neck reminded him. He tried to swing round but a second blow knocked him to the ground. A skin-swathed foot came into his eyeline and he jumped and twisted as another blow tipped him over into blackness. By the time he recovered consciousness the old couple had fled. They decided not to wait until his liver exploded, just grabbed what they could and ran.

De Palfrey dragged himself to his room and collapsed. The next time he awoke it was the middle of the night. In the black void Essodena's screams had a tangible quality. Like steely cobwebs drawn unceasingly over his nerve ends. He waved his hands in front of his face trying, with mounting futility, to brush the tormenting sound away. Driven almost insane he rushed from the room and once more directed his stumbling feet to the cellar. He was halfway down the steps before he noticed anything wrong. Instead of the darkness he expected there was a light, whiter and brighter than anything he had ever seen before. De Palfrey clung to the wall and peered down. Everything seemed to be as it should be.

Just the strange light that seemed to come from no particular source. Even as he watched it faded until it was only a steady glow. Emboldened by the comforting shadows on the staircase de Palfrey eased forward until he could see around the corner to the bricked-in alcove. What he saw made his hair stand on end, squeezed his heart until it was in danger of stopping.

Huddled around the new brickwork were a shadowy group. They were painstakingly removing the stonework, piece by piece. For a moment de Palfrey thought that the servants had called in some of the neighbours to investigate the disappearance of his wife and the soldiers and the ghastly screams that had been heard throughout the castle since that time – and still continued unabated. Fear put new resolve into him. If he was only dealing with a handful of servants he would soon sort them out.

Cautiously he inched down the last few steps and picked up a shoulder-high, iron candlestick from the floor. It was a little base-heavy but as the Count balanced it in his hand and eyed the figures at the wall he estimated that he could make a bloody mess of them without much trouble.

Essodena's screams were louder now and they seemed to have more urgency than before, as if she knew what he had in mind and was warning her rescuers to hurry. De Palfrey smiled to himself as he edged up behind them. He was about to strike when he noticed the wall. All the time he had been watching the dim figures had been busily taking the stones away. Yet there was no hole. The wall was as solid as when he had first put it up. Astonishment stopped his hand. He looked at the half-dozen human shapes in front of him. He could see right through them! A bright light, brighter than anything he had seen before, flared out, banishing the phantom workers. As the light dimmed they appeared again, patiently taking bricks from the wall, which stayed solid.

De Palfrey could feel his reason deserting him. He no longer cared what happened to him. All he wanted was the hideous screaming to stop and he knew that to still it he must destroy the ghosts working against him. Desperately he swung the iron candlestick, knowing that it would not affect the fate being played out before him. Another, deeper, more melodious sound started up, underscoring the screamed cadenzas. De Palfrey saw another figure appear by the side of the workers. It appeared to be robed in white. It was from this spectre that the chanting came. The Count backed away. He felt that the new menace was directed at him. In terror he drew back his arm and threw the candlestick. Again the terrible white light swelled out, battering his senses. As his light-blinded eyes cleared he saw the candlestick lying on the floor by the wall. It had passed right through the ghostly figures without touching them. But now their white, blurred faces were turned in his direction and they emanated an aura of destruction. Count de Palfrey could stand it no longer. His mind could no longer cope with the hellish scene made more dreadful by Essodena's screams and the primeval chant of the white devil. He turned to run to safety up the stone steps. He had almost reached their sanctuary when he was aware of yet another figure on his right. This one appeared to have one enormous eye in the top of his head. De Palfrey hesitated, unwilling to go near the phantom cyclops. He was still staring in fatal fascination when the eye erupted once more with the white light that delivered a physical blow. Blinded once more, Count Roger de Palfrey blundered away from the lacerating light. As his foot trod into space he remembered the open seige well.

Too late!

He tried to throw himself sideways to evade the black hole trying to suck him down – but he was too late! Essodena's screams stopped suddenly as his flailing body disappeared into the well but, as Count de Palfrey tumbled downwards to join the bodies of his victims, he heard her voice again.

But now her screams had turned to peals of laughter!

*

Canon Sean Tompson carefully laid his bible in his leather briefcase and removed his white surplice. He was pleased at the way the service had gone. It was always a bit chancy doing an exorcism. The action was open to so much misinterpretation. He folded his surplice and cassock carefully and placed them in his duffle bag before slipping a sweater on to complement his worn jeans. In the cellar the rest of the group were packing their tools away and getting ready to leave. Sean went across to where they had taken the wall away and peered in. The cobwebbed skeleton in the chair seemed to be looking right at him, the yellow skull canted back at an angle that opened the jaw in a silent scream.

The Canon shivered and backed away. He saw Professor Culver, the leader of the archaeological party, looking at him and gave a wry smile. Culver hadn't wanted the church in on the excavation but as the castle had been used as a monastery for 400 years he hadn't much choice in the matter. There had been enough corroborated sightings to make the committed ghost-hunter believe that Castle de Palfrey was haunted. Not just visually but aurally as well. Since the nineteenth century onwards, when everything was ordained to have a rational explanation, scientists had tried to prove that the frightened screams and gurgling laughter were only the result of the wind through the decaying brickwork. Canon Tompson bent and gingerly picked up the heavy iron candlestick and examined it.

"I think the poor soul will be at rest now," he said. The professor nodded towards the skeleton.

"That poor soul has rested in there for about 500 years.

How much longer does she need?"

Sean shrugged.

"Once her bones rest in consecrated ground it will be finished." Culver lit a cigarette and went across to the photographer. He didn't want to get into an argument with the churchman but he knew it was inevitable if he talked to him for long. He also thought that he was excavating more than bricks and mortar but he resented the Canon's self-assured belief that it was understandable only through clerical interpretation. He wanted more practical evidence to supplement archaeological fact. Culver waited until the photographer had snapped the lock on his camera case and offered him a cigarette.

"Did you get anything?" he asked.

The photographer gave a thin smile. "I don't know until I've developed the film. These special plates are a bit tricky. You never know what you've got until they're developed," he said.

"If I'd wanted evidence for the judiciary I would have brought a barrister with me not a photographer," the professor said sharply.

"Guess I've got a little," the photographer flushed. "Well – I got the candlestick flying across the room – I think! And ..." his voice trailed away.

"Go on," Professor Culver snapped.

"Well! I kept thinking I could see a figure standing just by the bottom of the steps. He seemed to be watching as you broke through the wall." The photographer finished with an apologetic laugh.

"Did you get a photograph?" the professor asked with a rare note of excitement in his voice. The photographer ducked his head. "I don't know. I shot off a few flashes but as I said I won't ..."

Professor Culver didn't want to hear anymore. The photographer had confirmed what he had seen. A spectral figure that had stood watching them had tried to stop them and had then disappeared down the well.

Culver stood on the side of the newly reopened well and peered down. He couldn't see anything in the dark but he now knew what he must do. Tomorrow they would start on plumbing the depths of the well!

*

As the little group of archaeologists drove away Count Roger de Palfrey stood on the battlements of his castle and tried to ignore the screams of his entombed wife that echoed around the bare walls of the castle.

17
Casting Out Demons

Water witches, crowned with reeds
Bear me to your lethal tide.
I die; I come; my true love waits.
Thus the damsel spake, and died.

Thomas Chatterton *Song From Aella*

WHEN CHRIST WAS casting out demons he had a relatively easy task. For one thing he was the son of God, so any wrong-minded demon would want to give him a wide berth, and, for another, they were under the control of the Devil and, presumably made in his image. Ghosts aren't like that so they are much harder to identify and exorcise. Finding some ritual or incantation to get rid of an unfriendly spirit is a part of most religions from the Aborigines to the custodians of the Holy Catholic church. It can be anything from a simple spit on the toe of your boot and turning round three times when the moon is full, to liberating the unquiet soul through decapitation of the host. The latter was once very popular in Mexico City – along with all the other rites, fertility or otherwise.

Particularly hard to get rid of is the multiple possession. In this the poor host has not just one but many personalities sharing his or her body and they are not necessarily compatible. Take the case of Doris Fischer. The case was first brought to light by an Episcopalian minister called Franklin Prince in 1890. She was what would now be known as an abused child. On the surface Doris Fischer's father was a typical Victorian, strict but fair. In reality he was a bloody tyrant. Once the front door was safely closed on the hypocritical *belle époch* world, he was straight into the whisky. He didn't have to drink a lot before the sadistic side of his nature came to the fore. His wife, a weak character whose energy had been dissipated and her moral sensibilities corrupted by an adulthood of pregnancy, was in no shape to defend her children. As the savagery of the beatings increased and sexual abuse became the norm, Doris retreated into herself where she felt she had some sort of control. At first she just imagined herself as a sort of cross between an elf and an angel: an inner person, above the sordid abuse meted out by her drunken father and tacitly condoned by her weary mother. She began to tell fey tales of what she hoped might be her future. She finally got her father's attention when she forecast the death of her mother and it happened just the way she said. This didn't exactly endear her to her father who, now that any restraining influence, however negative, had been lost by the death of his wife, redoubled the alcoholic attacks on his children. It was a nightmare world and Doris sank deeper and deeper into it. This proved to be the opportunity the ever-vigilant ghost world was waiting for. Two different and distinct alter egos took over. One she acknowledged as "Sick Doris" and the other as "Wicked Margaret". Sick Doris was the personality that took over when her father was on the loose. Wicked Margaret asserted herself when it was pay-back time. In the end it was the father's need to appear to be just your regular guy that brought the sad case of Doris and her siblings out into the open. Reverend Prince, the minister, worried by the change in the appearance of Mr Fischer since the death of his wife, came calling. Doris was in the possession of Wicked Margaret at the time and the good doctor realised that here was more than just a case of an abused child trumpeting a cry for help. She was, without a doubt, possessed by evil spirits. Hadn't he just read a learned thesis on multiple possession? Wasn't this just the sort of case that he had been warned about?

Prince didn't think anyone was likely to listen to him if he started recounting his experiences so he got in touch with the president of the American Society for Psychical Research, H. Hyslop. Hyslop was getting on in years but he knew a good possession when he heard about it and was soon ringing Prince's doorbell and demanding in. Hyslop's credentials as a psychic researcher were a bit iffy but he had hedged his bets by acknowledging that cases where possession was suspected could be affected by so-called psychic cures. This meant diving into the maelstrom of a disordered mind, identifying what might be physically causing the disorder, then connecting the subject up to a couple of high-voltage electrodes and burning the nasty bits out of the victim's psyche. Whatever was left over was obviously beyond our ken and so could safely be labelled as some sort of supernatural interaction. Hyslop wanted to sort out what was what. He took Doris to see a well-known medium, Minnie Coule. Minnie specialised in separating the tangle of personalities living in one brain pan and tagging them for future reference. How much Minnie Coule was told about Doris's condition before the seance isn't known but it didn't take her long to flip out and start conveying messages to Doris from her dear departed mother. Uncaring her mother may have been in life but she had learned her lesson and in death she was very solicitous about her daughter's wellbeing.

The communications from her dead mother appear to have been the trigger for others, isolated on the astral plane and in need of an earthly interpreter, to get through. First up on the spiritual network was an Italian count called Cagliostro. Being a noble and an Italian to boot, his interest in the teenage girl was on the same level as her father's. His graphic suggestions and abusive language were a little ripe even for Hyslop and the medium hastily gave the astral tuner a flip, but not before making a mental note of the count's frequency for future reference. Next up was Richard Hodgson. In life he had been a devoted member of the Physical Research Society who could be relied upon to tell it as it was. In the afterlife he was a priceless contact. Through Minnie Coule, Hodgson confirmed that the unfortunate Doris Fischer was, in absolute fact, the battleground for a number of restless spirits who had unlocked the entry to her spiritual being and could now play as fast and loose with it as their sense of haunting permitted. Now Hyslop thought he had cracked it. His patient was a classic case of multiple personality. Now all he had to do was divide and exorcise.

Then Minnihaha came on the scene.

As every third former knows, Minnihaha's name translates as "Laughing Water" and, appropriately she lived by the shining big sea waters of Mitchigoomi. She was also a bit stuck on Hiawatha. Hiawatha reciprocated the feeling but was a fellow, so had to dress it up a bit. Redskins, ghost dances and the mystic prairie with their ghostly buffalo and spirit places were a literary goldmine in the early days of the twentieth century and Minnie Coule rather blotted her ethereal copybook by bringing on the Indian Minnie's spirit. Hyslop patiently explained to the surprised psychic that you couldn't believe all you read. Minnihaha may have appeared to be a living, breathing person but she was the invention of Henry Wordsworth Longfellow so it was a touch difficult to believe she could project a spirit into the hereafter and even more difficult to believe that said spirit could get on the line and offer advice on how to lay other troublesome spirits to rest. Minnie Coule was equal to the challenge to her veracity. Silly Hyslop was overlooking a basic point where spirits are concerned. Just because they didn't have a real existence in this mundane world didn't preclude them from taking on an alma in the next. It must have been a good argument: the gregarious Dr Hyslop fell for it and continued to work with her. It was the very intangibility of Minnihaha's spirit, Madame Coule explained, that made her such a catch as a connection through to the afterlife. She wasn't bothered with a soul. Hyslop had to agree that the previously unembodied Indian maid did seem to know quite a lot about the Fischer case. He apologised for his churlishness in doubting her and tuned into the Laughing Waters for the latest update on the Fischer problem. It now seemed that Minnihaha had been badly misjudged and had been a living, breathing, hide-chewing mate of Hiawatha in the eighteenth century when he was the war chief of the Iroquois. She had been sadly overlooked by history but the divine Longfellow had got on her case and resurrected her. Hyslop was suitably contrite but Minnie Coule reported darkly that Minnihaha was not so easily mollified and had actively taken a stance against Doris Fischer. Coule went further. She definitely laid the root of all Doris's troubles at the moccasins of the fractious Indian maid. Count Cagliostro couldn't be forgotten either. Although Minnihaha had overall control and dictated the extent and shape of the hauntings it was the licentious

Count who gathered together other discontented spirits and made astral commando raids on the long-suffering girl.

Hyslop was in a bit of a cleft stick with this one. He could make himself look a right idiot if it became known that he was spending good exorcism time trying to get rid of what most right-thinking people considered to be nothing more than a popular poet's fetid imagination of what it must be like to be the sex object of a sixteenth-century Native American. Coule decided to take on Count Cagliostro instead.

By this time Doris had been rescued from the predations of her father and had gone to live with the Episcopalian minister who had first recognised her as a combination of troubled spirits, Franklin Prince and his wife. Prince had kept in close touch with what was going on and when he heard what Hyslop intended to do offered his house as a temple for the ritual exorcism. Exorcisms, as mentioned earlier, come in all shapes and sizes. As befits an Episcopalian minister in America the casting out was done with total authority, much shouting, repeated Bible waving and frantic cries for God the Father, God the Son or God the Holy Ghost, to intervene. Whoever it was that he got in touch with was in a benign mood and gave Count Cagliostro his marching orders. Minihaha, without the sexually motivated Count to carry out her orders, went back to being a much loved character in an epic poem and Sick Doris and Wicked Margaret took a drastically reduced part in Doris's future. She went to California with the Princes and tried to recover from the depredations of her years as an astral switchboard but she was always a connection waiting to be made and would often relapse into being nothing more than a conduit to be used by any passing disorderly spirit. The Princes, mindful of the fact that their names would be written up by future generations of ghostbusters and that any relapse on Fisher's part might be seen as a failure on theirs, kept up the show of her recovery for years. Unfortunately Doris Fischer's mental

state deteriorated and, when the Princes could no longer hide her lunacy from the many enquirers interested in her case, stuck her in a mental institute and washed their hands of her. She died shortly after.

The Princes disappeared from the case but James Hyslop wrote a book about the Fischer phenomenon entitled imaginatively *Life after Death* (1918). He also stuck with Minnie Coule as his interlocutor between this world and the world of lost souls. When he later fell ill Minnie convinced him that it was the work of one of the spirit characters he had been pursuing through the ether. This proved to him that he had scientifically tested the existence of an afterlife and found that not only did it exist but that it had a not inconsiderable influence on the crude, three-dimensional world we live in.

*

Ghost stories are often closely connected to transport. Horse-drawn carriages rocketing through the night with headless drivers or horses, fire-breathing gallopers, with cloaked riders, very often headless, proving that they were either highwaymen or horse thieves before the axe fell or the rope plucked off their head, phantom planes or planes with phantom passengers, trains rushing through tunnels with all doors banging, ships causing dismay on the high seas, cars on a kamikaze course with brick walls and just about every other combination of mobility and fatality that can be imagined.

Cloaked or headless horsemen from the golden age of haunting are understandable. They are romantic and pre-TV. Aeroplane ghosts are a little harder to understand. This is the cutting edge of technology. Where do ghosts fit in? The answer is – everywhere! Most hauntings are the result of a crash, or some other trauma in the air. *The Boy* wasn't confined to just one site ...

18
The Boy

When wee are shadowes both ...

John Donne *Elegie: His Picture*

ROGER KNIGHT WALKED along the echoing corridor with precision. It was as much for his own benefit as for anyone who might happen to see him. For the umpteenth time he rubbed his hand across his chin and tried to convince himself that the growth wasn't too bad. Outside the door marked "Flight Planning and Met" he stopped and made a last effort to straighten the creases in his crumpled uniform and put some vitality into his legs. It was a vain attempt. The effects of sleeping in the back of a ten-year-old Ford Fiesta were not erased as easily as that. He ran a furry tongue along dry lips and considered going to the toilet and soothing his nerves with the half-bottle of White Horse he carried in his flight bag. He shook his head angrily. Appearing in the cockpit stinking of stale sweat and booze today wasn't on. The cards of his career were already trembling and it wouldn't need much of a breeze to send them tumbling.

Captain Paul Bernard was already in the room checking over his flight plan. John Grayson, the engineer, was perched on the corner of a table chatting to a stewardess. Neither acknowledged Knight's presence as he slumped into a vacant seat opposite Bernard and pulled the folder with the photostat copies of Europe's weather towards him. He didn't care. Repeated liberal doses of alcohol had long ago burned out the necessity for friendship. Besides he had always regarded Bernard

as a bit of a slob. He was in his mid-thirties now, at the apex of his career and had got as far as he was going to go. Knight was better than that. He had reached the heights in his profession, was even being considered for the right-hand seat in Concorde. Then everything had gone wrong. From being an asset to the airline, he had become a liability. A drunken shambling figure, avoided by the other pilots and despised by the cabin crew. For a while he was able to keep his job based on his previous record. But gradually he sunk down the greasy pole as he was dismissed by one company after the other for bringing less than professional expertise to his job.

Until Omega Freightways and the right-hand seat as co-pilot. The shock helped to pull Knight together for a while. Then his personal phantoms returned. Knight was halfway up the gangway when he suddenly stopped. The two men behind him looked at each other and continued to climb the steps. It was a familiar pattern and one that had brought Knight to the end of his career. Bernard knew what Knight only suspected. With that month's cheque would be coming yet another dismissal notice. And after Omega there was no place to go. Roger Knight forced himself to mount the remaining steps to the fuselage door. He told himself that he had seen nothing. That it was all a figment of his imagination. He always told himself that. It was no good. His brain worked on two levels – both uncompromisingly suspicious of the other. Intellectually he knew that what ailed him was a mentally projected image focused by guilt. Which was fine if he could live with it. Unfortunately the more primitive part of his personality was capable of shattering any cosy psychological argument by tapping straight into his nerve centre. So, whereever he went, there was the small figure of a boy, smiling and friendly, to bring back the horror.

Roger went through the pre-flight checks mechanically. The familiar routine helped. Gradually he relaxed and by the time they had reached their flight level at 8.000 feet for the first leg he felt fitter than he had for a long time. In the permanent sunshine above the clouds, the muted roar of the engines, the calm, routine voices piercing the static, Knight could believe that the last five years didn't exist. That Fran and Jake were still alive and he was a skipper again ferrying important people to important destinations.

Jake!

He had been the first to go.

Eaten up with guilt! Roger had read all the books on psychology that he could find and he still wasn't sure who had raised the phantom. Was it Jake? Had his conscience been so outraged that it had hypnotised Fran and him in some way? Or was it possible that the image that had led him to his death was still there, waiting for more victims? Or was he the source? His was the greater guilt! Had he mesmerised his companions so that they were filled by his ghosts? And their deaths? Did their deaths make the boy more substantial to him?

As the Comet passed the French coast and climbed to its onward level, Roger once again went over the traumatic events that had brought him to his present position. Fran had been a stewardess. She had filled in the grey when his wife had left him and taken their son Domenico back to live in Rome with her family. Donatella's desertion hadn't worried him. He wasn't

even sure that the loss of his son was such a big thing. But it rankled! He felt he should do something about it. Fran was sympathetic and listened to his schemes to get his son back without comment. She realised it was only his ego talking and sooner or later he would adjust to the situation. He almost had!

Then he got into a ridiculous argument with his wife. They were on a night stopover in Rome. Roger had phoned and made arrangements to take Domenico out. It was now almost a year since he had separated from Donatella and Fran had become part of his life. It didn't occur to him that his wife might object to her presence.

Roger had taken Domenico and Fran to an early cinema show and afterwards to Frascati's in the Piazza di Popolo for an early meal. Domenico was just eight years old and ready for bed early. Donatella had arranged to pick Domenico up at the airport in the morning. Roger left him with Fran while he checked in. When he went to look for them he knew he was in trouble. Domenico had blurted out to his mother what they had done the evening before and that he had spent the night on a couch in the same room as his father and Fran. Donatella, a true Roman matron, flew straight to the attack. In a strident voice so that everybody on the concourse could hear, she described Fran's descent into whoredom in colourful phraseology. Roger did his best to quieten her but she wasn't prepared to be mollified. Domenico started to cry and begged them to stop but they were too far gone in their vilification of each other to notice. Jake finally broke the battle up and separated the feuding parties.

But the incident had hurt Knight. It brought back all his feelings of inadequacy as far as his son was concerned. Fran took his wild vows of revenge as nothing more than hot air – trying to save face after the embarrassment of the public affray at the airport.

A week later, en route for Rome airport once more, he told Jake and Fran what he intended to do. They tried to talk him out of it but he insisted that as Domenico's father he had a right to take him away from a mother who was obviously unfit to bring him up. There were no legal problems. Donatella's strict Catholicism put divorce out of the question and there was no legal reason why Domenico should be with his mother rather than his father. Reluctantly they agreed to go along with him.

Roger rang Donatella and said he wanted to see her at the airport. To apologise! He wasn't specific about what he was going to apologise for, leaving his wife to fill in the blanks. He also asked her to bring Domenico. She wasn't too happy about that at first but he finally persuaded her.

Fran kept well out of the way at the airport. Roger wasn't taking any chances on provoking another scene. Jake came along with him and when Roger suggested to Donatella that they went to one of the quieter areas to talk, the second officer offered to take Domenico out to the aircraft to have a look at it. Domenico was so enthusiastic that it would have been difficult for Donatella to stop him even if she had wanted to. Roger kept Donatella talking until ten minutes before his flight was due to leave. She didn't know this and when he excused himself and headed for the toilets she had no reason to suspect anything.

Once out of sight Roger headed for the Boeing.

Jake had already completed the checks and as Roger joined him got start-up clearance.

Domenico was standing in the cockpit. He smiled happily when he saw his father arrive but became worried when it was obvious that preparations were in hand to leave. He tried to question his father but Roger was too involved to spare him any time. He called Fran forward and told her to look after the boy.

Domenico didn't like that. His mother's reaction to the smiling stewardess had fostered an unreasoning fear and he was unwilling to go along with her. Impatiently Roger ordered Fran to take him from the cockpit. Against his violent protests she dragged him out and shut the door. The gangway had just been withdrawn and a steward was about to close the door when Donatella appeared on the scene. When Roger hadn't returned she had become suspicious. Her first thoughts had been for the boy. As she saw him in the doorway struggling with Fran she screamed his name. The stewardess was startled and in that split second Domenico had torn himself from her grip and dashed blindly towards the sound of his mother's voice.

The 25-foot drop to the concrete below killed him!

Roger Knight had been censured by the airline and lost some seniority but as Domenico was his son the matter was dropped.

Donatella tried to get a murder charge made out against him but even in the tricky Italian courts the accident was seen as just another of life's little tragedies and nothing was done.

Jake was the first to break down. Roger noticed a fall in efficiency. At first he just put it down to a sort of aftershock. When, instead of recovering, Jake became more disorganised and careless, he took him to task. It required a lot of persuasion to get Jake to talk. At last Jake confessed that since Domenico was killed in Rome airport his dreams had been filled with the boy. That he could cope with! Now there was a new dimension. He was seeing the boy in the flesh. Roger tried to reason with him, to convince him that it was nothing more than a hallucination. Jake agreed but it did nothing to exorcise the spectre.

A few nights later they were leaving a restaurant on the Via Veneto when Jake gripped Roger's arm and pointed across the busy street.

Roger saw nothing.

Just the usual throng of sightseers getting a vicarious thrill from being on one of Rome's notoriously romantic streets. Whatever was getting Jake into such a state was outside the normal vision of the others.

Roger gripped Jake's arm. His co-pilot was clearly on the borders of some sort of seizure. His eyes were wild and bulging, the white visible all around the iris. His jaw was working as if he was trying to get rid of a particularly tacky toffee that was stuck on his back teeth. Roger tried to force Jake away from whatever was exciting him but he pushed him away and pointed across the street, desperately trying to make his companions see what he saw.

"There! Look! You must see! It's Domenico! See – he's waving to us ..! Please, please – say you see him!!"

In spite of Jake's begging neither of them were able to calm him by claiming to see his vision. They tried to hustle him away, he was beginning to attract a circle of sightseers. With another wild exhortation for them to see Domenico he pushed Fran to the ground, wrenched his arm from Roger's grasp and dashed into the road. He was nearly across when a motor-scooter hit him. It spun him round and knocked him off his balance. He sprawled in the road. Before he could get back on his feet a florist van hit him, pushing his body several feet before crushing it up against the kerb.

Jake was dead by the time Roger got to him. He called for a doctor knowing it was no use. As he looked desperately around the crowd he thought for a moment he saw a small boy, standing between the legs of the adults, laughing at him. He tried to get a better look but the crowd had shifted and the boy gone. He didn't tell Fran what he had seen, nor did he admit to himself that the boy reminded him of Domenico. But he remembered it a few days later when Fran told him that she thought she had seen Domenico. It frightened him although he ridiculed the suggestion and accused her of letting Jake's wild talk get to her. She smiled but Roger could see the effort it took. Roger felt a hand on his arm and looked

up. Paul Bernard was leaning towards him and he wasn't looking pleased.

"You're supposed to be on duty, Mr Knight," he said pedantically. "Try to stay awake!"

Roger started to protest that he hadn't been asleep but the captain wasn't interested.

"I've asked you twice to go and check the cargo. Are you going to do it or should I send Mr.Grayson?"

Roger snapped the catch on his safety belt and swivelled out of his seat without protest. Grayson was watching him and he guessed that as soon as he left the flight deck his two colleagues would pass a few disparaging remarks about his conduct. He shrugged and muttered to himself as he pushed open the door and stepped into the chilly atmosphere of the cargo deck.

What did he care?

A movement off to the right made him catch his breath but when he swung round there was nothing there. It was a familiar pattern. The flicker at the limits of his peripheral vision that somehow translated into the form of a small laughing boy. Roger fixed his attention on the sacks of evil-smelling bran preparation bound for the stables of an Italian race-horse trainer who hoped to transform this stock of mediocre mares by feeding them the same diet as one of Britain's most successful stables. Everything was in order so Roger sat on one of the soft sacks and lit an illicit cigarette. As he watched the smoke he thought of Fran. She had always been trying to give up smoking but had never been able to master it. The smoking had got worse after Jake's death. Her nerve had gone completely. It had led to bad scenes between them. They had stopped sharing the same accommodation on stopovers. Fran said it was to give her a chance to pull herself together but Roger wasn't fooled. Fran had never been a drinker but suddenly she needed it to help her through the day. Initially it gave her a few high moments but as the dosage and reliance increased so did the post-alcoholic depressions. Roger talked it over with her and they had come to a decision. Whatever the reason, Fran's problem was aggravated by Roger's presence. She couldn't get Domenico's death out of her mind. It made her nervous and often hysterical. That's all – it was simple hysteria. But that didn't make the fact that she constantly thought she saw Domenico any less harrowing. They decided that in future they would schedule their flights so that they saw less of each other. Their last flight was to be Rome. They both booked in at the Meridiana, in separate rooms, and agreed to have a last meal together before their final flight in the morning. At eight o'clock Roger was about to knock on her door when he heard her scream out.

"NO! NO Domenico - NOOO!"

There was a loud bang from within the room, the lights in the corridor dimmed momentarily and Roger heard the sound of something falling. He tried the door. It was unlocked.

"Fran?" he said, frightened in spite of himself. As he stepped into the room he thought he saw a small figure run out onto the balcony. As he bent down beside Fran's inert body and felt for her pulse he fancied he heard a gleeful chuckle of boyish laughter.

Fran was dead!

The police put it down to an electrical fault. She had been pressing her uniform with a small travel iron she always carried and technical opinion was that the wet cloth was in some way a contributory factor in her electrocution. Although they admitted themselves baffled. There did not appear to be a fault in the iron.

Roger finished his cigarette and carefully extinguished it and hid it away where the parsimonious Bernard wasn't likely to spot it. As he bundled himself back into his seat he heard Rome control pass instructions for approach to Leonardo da Vinci airport. He had heard it countless times before but since the accident the softly spoken instructions bringing the aircraft safely into land had a special dark significance. The return flight was scheduled for the following morning. The crew booked themselves in at one of the small hotels near the airport. The in-town luxury hotels were not for Omega pilots. Nobody asked Roger to join them for dinner so he stayed in his room. He preferred it that way. He realised that it was admitting defeat. In the restaurant some of the time would be taken up with conversation and eating. In the solitude of his room there was just him and the half-bottle of White Horse to which he intended to limit himself. By 10.30 he was asleep. Several times during the long night he sat up with a jerk, sure that he had heard Domenico's childish laughter in the room. It was 4 o'clock when he finally abandoned all thoughts of sleeping further. Awake or asleep his son seemed to be there, calling, laughing, playing games. As he had a million times before, Knight explained to himself that it was all a figment of his imagination brought on by guilt. That the deaths of Jake and Fran were nothing more than accidents. But even as he presented his reasoned argument, more primitive voices subtly suggested that it was impossible for three people to see something if it didn't exist. Argument and counter-argument surged through his brain until he felt sick and confused. He cursed his lack of forethought in not providing a second bottle for emergencies. A foray into the kitchen unearthed a sleeping night-porter who grudgingly came up with two miniature bottles of Scotch, a gin and a brandy. Roger downed the Scotch where he stood and then sauntered back to his room with the booty.

In the dim light of the corridor he saw the tiny, phantom figure standing outside his room. Fortified by the Scotch he didn't falter. As he got nearer the shadow resolved into a normal earthly shadow made by the low light and the recessed door. Roger chuckled confidently to himself. It was what he always knew it was. A natural phenomena given an unearthly significance by his neurotic brain.

The small bottles consumed in rapid succession calmed him down and by the time he was called at 7.30 he felt much better. He stood under the cold shower until he shivered. As much as he needed it he was unable to face breakfast so he waited, hunched in his uniform, in the tiny reception until the other two were ready. At the airport he fortified himself with a double Scotch and then went through to the flight-planning office and met the others. There was nothing for him to do. He tried to chat to Bernard but got only monosyllabic replies. Their flight plan safely filed they left the office and made their way to the aircraft. Bernard and Grayson went aboard leaving Knight to do the exterior inspection to see that they still had their full complement of wings and that there were no foreign objects like a fuel bowser lodged in the engine. Roger took his time about the inspection. He was enjoying an unusual feeling of wellbeing in the morning sun. His calm was shattered as he started to climb the steps. A giggle made him look fearfully up. Perched on the top step was Domenico. This time there was no doubt! He was there, within a dozen feet in the bright morning sunlight. This was no dark fleeting figure that could be given another construction.

"Domenico!" Roger sobbed in terror. The little boy stood up and looked down at his father with a look of sorrow. Slowly he shook his head and then turned and disappeared through the door into the plane. Roger pulled himself together. "Domenico!" he called and ran up the remaining steps. At the door he almost collided with Grayson who had been sent to see what was keeping him. Grayson drew a long-suffering breath and went back to the flight deck. Frantically Roger looked around the cargo cabin. The return cargo was cases of auto-spares. The wooden crates were packed high and secured with nets and thick canvas straps. The captain's angry voice claimed

Roger's attention and he left the cargo and went onto the flight deck and strapped himself in. But not before he heard a soft, mocking chuckle from the deep shadows at the back of the cargo hold. Desperately he tried to focus his mind on the work in hand but several times Bernard savagely called his attention to mistakes.

At last they were airborne.

As Roger brought the wheels up he gave a sigh of unreasonable relief. Now that they were no longer in contact with Italian soil he felt that he had avoided the worst of his problems. By the time they had reached their cruising level Roger was feeling quite relaxed. He dismissed his earlier fears as nothing more than nerves.

When Bernard told him to go back and check that the cargo had not shifted during their climb out he welcomed the distraction. It also gave him an opportunity to take a swig at the bottle he kept hidden in reserve behind the fire extinguishers. His fingers had just closed around the neck of the bottle when a voice made him spin round with a cry of terror.

"Daddy!"

Domenico was sitting on one of the crates. He smiled when he saw he had his father's attention. Roger forgot about the bottle and tried to run for the cabin door. His legs refused to function.

"Daddy!" the soft childish voice called again and Domenico jumped down off the box so that he was standing between Roger and the door into the flight deck. Knight felt his reason deserting him. He knew beyond any doubt that his son was dead! That what he saw before him was just a spectre conjured up out of his own deranged imagination. But the boy was too strong, too insistent to ignore.

"Domenico!" he sobbed, "I'm sorry. I didn't mean to hurt you!"

Domenico smiled and held out his arms. Without thought Roger stumbled forward. Just as Roger was

THE BOY

about to take his son in his arms the boy slipped away with a giggle and dodged between the packing cases.

Roger followed!

The boy led his father a dance through the cramped cargo hold, always staying just out of reach but drawing the demented man onwards with a soft giggle or an endearment. For a moment Roger thought he had lost him. Then he spotted him sitting high on one of the stacked cases.

"Come down, Domenico – before you hurt yourself," he ordered.

The boy laughed and impishly shook his head.

"Come down at once or I'll come and get you," Roger said in mock anger. Slowly and provocatively the boy shook his head.

"Right!" shouted Roger with a laugh, making a game of it. The boy didn't move as he clambered over the heavy cases. He had almost reached him when the plane hit an air pocket and bucked like a gigantic bronco. Roger heard the mounting securing one of the cases snap as he fought to keep his balance. There was an agonising pain in his leg as the shifting boxes pinned him down. As he struggled to free his leg Domenico leaned forward to get a better look at what was happening.

"Domenico! Help me!" Roger pleaded.

Domenico stood up on the highest box and began to laugh. Gone was the pure innocence of his 8-year-old face. Now there was a harshness and a malign threat that terrified the trapped man. The plane was still being thrown about by the turbulence and Roger could hear the creaks and groans as the stresses on the shifting cargo became more excessive. He tried to shout for the pilot but the engine sound drowned out his cry. With a scream he felt the crate shift and slowly but inexorably crush his leg. He heard the sound of the snapping bone above the demonic sound of the boy's laughter, which seemed to fill the cabin with solid menace. The case on his right began to move towards him. Almost fainting with pain he tried to avert the danger by pushing the crate away from him. He couldn't get enough leverage and it inched forward squeezing him in a remorseless vice. He felt ribs snap and tasted blood in his mouth.

The boy was hysterical with laughter, rolling around on the packing case just above Roger's head, each new development provoking increased merriment.

"Domenico!" Roger whispered. "Help me!"

Suddenly the laughter stopped. Domenico leaned down until his face was almost level with his father's.

"Help you Daddy?" he asked in an earnest, serious voice. He looked at the encroaching crates as if seeing them for the first time.

"Help you?" he smiled and nodded as if only just appreciating the situation. He stood up on the case.

"I'll help you." He began to laugh again. At the same time he began to jump up and down.

"I'll help you! I'll help you!" he sang out as he jumped. Slowly, as the packing case tilted and tipped over to crush the trapped man, he heard the sound of the boy's laughter rise and swell until it filled the universe.

19
Portents

A little ere the mightiest Julius fell
The graves stood tenantless and the sheeted dead
Did squeak and gibber in the Roman streets

William Shakespeare *Hamlet*

MASTER BLIGH, a Cornwallian schoolboy, had an aversion to going to school. Not an unusual attitude for a youngster but this one had a reason that, at first, appeared to be beyond the run of excuses needed to avoid a whipping when arriving late in the classroom. He had, as he explained, been pestered by a ghost on his way to school on a number of occasions and that day, in an effort to avoid the disturbing encounter, he had taken the long route to school. Ergo – he was late! That little bit of poetic impertinence earned him six of the best but in spite of stinging palms and smarting pants he persisted with his story. As was usual at this time the county schools, especially in the west country, were run by the Church of England and came under the authority of the local vicar. The boy's parents, having more belief in their son's veracity than had his teacher, spruced themselves up in their Sunday best and presented themselves at the vicarage. The Reverend John Ruddle was more open-minded than the naturally sceptical schoolteacher and listened to Bligh's story with interest. The boy told him that as he was making his way along the path across the 20-acre field he met a woman who appeared to glide above the surface. She was dressed in flowing robes and at times he could see right through her. She kept gliding up to him and trying to say something but he was too overwrought to understand her words. He admitted that it had happened on a number of occasions but he hadn't mentioned it before because he was sure nobody would believe him. The vicar, not wanting to be amongst the disbelievers, agreed to accompany Bligh the following morning and see the apparition for himself.

The dew was still on the grass when the Reverend Ruddle went to the appointed place to meet the boy and his father. They took him to the field where the ghostly encounters had taken place and walked along the path. On schedule the spectre appeared and passed by them. The vicar called out to her but her mind, if ghosts have a mind, was preoccupied with higher thoughts and she didn't answer. Bligh and his father stayed with Ruddle for most of the morning but nothing notable happened. At last Mr Bligh had had enough and told the vicar he had work to do. The vicar also decided he was wasting his time. Obviously the apparition wasn't too keen on parading herself before the gawking yokels. Satisfied that Bligh junior had been telling the truth, backed by the evidence of his own eyes, he determined to return alone and confront the restless spirit. First he decided to try and identify who she was. By questioning the villagers he soon came to the conclusion that it was the shade of one Dorothy Dingle who had been considered a little fey by her neighbours and had recently passed away. Armed with this titbit of information the vigilant vicar dragged himself out of bed at the crack of dawn and made his way to the field. He hadn't long to wait. The ghostly wraith appeared at his side and seemed to be trying to tell him something. The vicar was petrified. Now he hadn't the support of a couple of his parishioners to bolster up his faith. But he was a man of character and persisted in his efforts to find out why Dorothy was making a bit of a nuisance of herself. The ghost tried to communicate but her voice was so low that Ruddle could only make out a few words, and these he didn't understand. Ruddle made up his mind. Something had to be done. He couldn't have a maverick apparition gliding around and frightening the parishioners. It was a case for the Bishop.

The Bishop wasn't too pleased that his once trustworthy underling was offering him an offertory box of dubious currency. Exorcism was alright for the papists but the Anglican church regarded it as a bit too salty for their taste. Reverend Ruddle had expected opposition and had prepared his case carefully. After an hour or two's wrangling he was able to convince his immediate ecclesiastical master that exorcism wasn't necessarily a bad thing. With the Bishop's reluctant blessing Ruddle returned to the village fully prepared to come to grips, bell, book and candle, with the disappearing presence. From Ruddle's diary we are able to extract the full flavour of his next and final meeting with the visionary ghost:

January 12th, 1665. Rode into the gateway of Botathen, armed at all points, but not with Saul's armour, and ready. There is danger from the demons, but so there is in the surrounding air every day. At early morning then and alone, for so the usage ordains, I betook me towards the field. It was void, and I had thereby due time to prepare. First I paced and measured out my circle on the grass. Then did I mark my pentacle in the very midst and at the intersection of the five angles I did set up and fix my crutch of rowan. Lastly I took my station south, at the true line of the meridian, and stood facing due north. I waited and watched for a long time. At last there was a kind of trouble in the air, a soft and rippling sound, and all at once the shape appeared, and came on towards me gradually. I opened my parchment scroll, and read aloud the command. She paused and seemed to waver and doubt; stood still: and then I rehearsed the sentence again, sounding out every syllable like a chant. She drew near my ring, but halted at first outside, on the brink. I sounded again, and now at the third time I gave the signal in Syriac – the speech which is used, they say, where such ones dwell and converse in thoughts that glide.

She was at last obedient and swam into the midst of the circle: and there stood still suddenly. I saw, moreover, that she drew back her pointing hand. All this while I do confess that my knees shook under me, and the drops of sweat ran down my flesh like rain. But now, although face to face with the spirit, my heart grew calm and my mind composed, to know that the pentacle would govern her, and the ring must bind until I gave the word. Then I called to mind the rule laid down of old that no angel or fiend, no spirit, good or evil, will ever speak until they be spoken to. N.B. – This is the great law of prayer. God Himself will not yield reply until man hath made vocal entreaty once and again. So I went on to demand, as the books advise; and the phantom made answer willingly. Questioned wherefore not at rest? Unquiet because of a certain sin. Asked what and by whom? Revealed it; but it is sub sigillo, and therefore nefas dictu; more anon. Inquired, what sign she could give me that she was a true spirit and not a false friend?

Stated (that) before next Yule-tide a fearful pestilence would lay waste the land; and myriads of souls would be loosened from their flesh, until, as she piteously said, "Our valleys will be full."

Asked again, why she so terrified the lad? Replied, "It's the law; we must seek a youth or a maiden of clean life, and under age, to receive messages and admonitions."

We conversed with many more words; but it is not lawful for me to set them down. Pen and ink would degrade and defile the thoughts she uttered and which my mind received that day. I broke the ring and she passed, but to return once more next day. At evensong a long discourse with that ancient transgressor, Mr B–. Great horror and remorse; entire atonement and penance; whatsoever I enjoin; full acknowledgement before pardon.

January 13, 1665. At sunrise I was again in the field. She came in at once, and, as it seemed, with freedom. Inquired if she knew my thoughts, and what I was going to relate? Answered, "Nay, we only know what we perceive and hear: we cannot see the heart."

Then I rehearsed the penitent words of the man she had come up to denounce, and the satisfaction he would perform. Then said she, "Peace in our midst."

I went through the proper forms of dismissal, and fulfilled all, as it was set down and written in my memoranda; and then with certain fixed rites, I did dismiss that troubled ghost, until she peacefully withdrew, gliding towards the west. Neither did she ever afterwards appear; but was allayed, until she shall come in her second flesh, to the Valley of Armageddon on the Last Day.

It's a nice, carefully controlled story that tactfully and tastefully doesn't go into what Mr B had been up to with the buxom Dottie Dingle before she shuffled off this mortal coil. Whatever it was, it was enough to have her gliding around and seeking out virgin boys to receive her confidences. Then there is the warning about the plague. Ruddle had something to say about this. In his diary on July 10th 1668 his quill ran hot with condemnation. Triumphalism in a priest is not a pretty emotion:

How sorely must the infidels and heretics of this generation be dismayed when they know that this Black Death, which is now swallowing its thousands in the streets of the great city, was foretold six months agone, under the exorcism of a country minister, by a visible and suppliant ghost! And what pleasures and improvements do such deny themselves who scorn and avoid all opportunity of intercourse with souls separate, and the spirits, glad and sorrowful, which inhabit the unseen world.

Of course the warning had been ignored. Who was going to take any notice when an unknown vicar in a little Cornish village warned that the mighty capital of London was to be devastated. Six months later, when the Black Death was at its height, Ruddles could only shake his head wisely and unctuously bemoan the fact that God had sent a messenger to warn of the peril about to be visited on them and nobody had been inclined to listen.

20
Trio of Death

The earth hath bubbles, as the water has,
And these are of them.

William Shakespeare *Macbeth*

CHRISTMAS IS ALWAYS a good time for ghost stories. It probably has something to do with the excitement of the ancient pagan rituals on which the Christian festival is based. It also has something to do with the customary overindulgence in food and wine. Overindulgence was enough to provide the inspiration Bram Stoker needed to pen the all-time favourite, *Dracula*, so why shouldn't less durable tales start with a surfeit of Christmas pud and Courvoisier? Not all the stories told around the yuletide log are meant to be taken as anything more than a morbid flight of the imagination to accompany the depression of the depth of winter. But there are those that claim to be true: this is one of them.

Maidenhead, as pretty as it is in summer, is depressing in the dark winter months. The cold winds follow the Thames from the North Sea and the almost permanent mist makes it an ideal setting for the appearance of restless souls. Or those about to become restless souls. It happened shortly after what was known enthusiastically as the Great War – the war to end wars or more plainly, World War I. Tony Andrews had been unfit to share in the slaughter in the trenches and had settled down to a quiet life in the family business of renting out row boats to the weekend visitors who wanted to test their muscles against the Thames. He was a placid, good-humoured,

unimaginative youth. His hero was his twin brother who had done everything he would have loved to do if he hadn't suffered ill-health from birth.

It was Christmas Eve and Tony lay in bed thinking about his brother and the excitement they had felt as they lay in bed trying to keep awake and surprise Father Christmas when he stepped from the chimney. His thoughts were distracted by the sound of running feet in the gravel outside his window. It wasn't an unusual sound. Revellers leaving the pub a quarter of a mile away often used the towpath as a shortcut home. Something about the sound drew Tony from his warm bed to the window. Pulling the curtain aside he was astounded to see a seaman, complete with peak cap, reefer jacket and thigh boots, running at breakneck speed towards the house. A break in the cloud illuminated the scene like day and Tony saw the face of the running man. It was his brother, Daniel. Happiness flooded through him. They were going to have their Christmas together after all. Daniel was a seafaring man and was meant to be thousands of miles away in South Africa. Obviously he had cut short the trip and returned home. Tony threw open the casement window and leaned out. The movement attracted the attention of the fleeing man. He called out desperately, "Save me! For God's sake – save me!" The cry sounded so desperate that Tony looked back along the tow path to see what could be the cause of his brother's fear. All he could see were three evil, distorted shadows that seemed to be homing in on Daniel. Before he could get through the gate the distorted forms were on him. They seemed to envelop him and, in spite of his vigorous attempts to break loose, and he was a powerful man, drag him away. Tony tried to cry out but a black impenetrable fog seemed to invade the room and enclose him, shutting off the air, wrapping him in a dark, clammy cocoon. Choking he felt himself falling and managed to scream out. His screams brought his mother and father running. He was lying on his bed, wild eyed, covered in sweat when they found him. Tony didn't want to distress them so he just told them he had experienced a nightmare and they all went back to sleep. To dream again. Once more he was able to jerk himself away from his terror. A third time he had the same disturbing dream. Tony decided that he was going to get no sleep that night so he got up and went and looked out of the window.

All was quiet!

Exactly as it had always been every other moonlit night that he could remember. He was about to go to the kitchen and get himself a drink when he again heard the sound of footsteps on the gravel towpath. This was not the scurrying rush of a frightened man but the measured tread of a confident man. Surprised that anyone should be on the path so early – it was now nearly dawn – Tony waited by the window to see who it was. He couldn't believe what he saw. It was his brother Daniel, clad as he had seen him earlier, but now there was no hint of fear as he approached the cottage gate. Tony wondered if he could be sleeping and pinched himself. The thought flitted across his mind that pinching was no clear indication of wakefulness but now his brother was through the gate and walking up the path. Eagerly Tom

opened the window and called down to him. Daniel made no reply. Again Tony called to him without result. Tony expected him to come in the front door but instead he turned away to the left on a little path that would take him around the back of the house to the shed were the boats were repaired. Tony assumed that for some reason best known to himself Daniel had decided to come in through the kitchen door. Maybe he was hungry and wanted to make himself a snack without waking the whole household. He threw on a coat and quietly went below. There was no sign of Daniel – anywhere!

Tony didn't know what to do. He was certain that he had been wide awake when he saw Daniel but couldn't explain what had happened to him once he had passed out of sight. At breakfast he carefully brought up Daniel's name and waited for his parents' reaction. They were sad that he was not there for Christmas and hoped that before long he would be back to see them. Tony realised that Daniel had not turned up and decided that he had, after all, been dreaming.

On New Year's Eve a telegram arrived from the captain of Daniel's ship. Briefly it stated that Daniel had been drowned while sleepwalking. The Andrews family was devastated. And mystified. They could never remember Daniel sleepwalking in his life. Tony was in a quandary. The date and time of Daniel's death was roughly the same time as when he had been plagued by his nightmares. He considered telling his parents but decided against it. It would be too distressing.

Daniel's father wrote back to the captain and asked for more details. The captain was not forthcoming. Andrews didn't let the matter drop there but pursued his enquiries at the shipping office and with the other members of the crew. Nothing seemed capable of shedding any light on the mystery of Daniel's death. Mr and Mrs Andrews died without ever solving the mystery of their son's death. Tony sold up the house and moved down the Thames to

TRIO OF DEATH

Greenwich. He was having a quiet drink in his local one night when the barman attracted his attention. He asked him if he had a twin brother called Daniel. Surprised, Tony confirmed that he had once had a brother called Daniel and wanted to know how the barman knew. The man pointed across to the far side of the bar and told him that the old gentleman sitting in the settle by the fire wanted to talk to him. Tony thanked the barman and went across to the other bar. The old man didn't look up as he approached, just sat hunched forward, staring into the embers. When Tony made himself known the old man gave a long shuddering sigh and waved him to a seat on the other side of the fireplace.

It took the old man, whose name was Richard Trew, a long time to gather his thoughts and the courage to tell his remarkable tale. It concerned his son, Jim. Jim had been a seaman and had recently died. Jim had sworn his father to secrecy but now that he was dead his father felt that he had been released from his oath and able to tell his son's extraordinary tale. Jim had been on deck watch one night in the port of Buenos Aires. The night had a chill and he was warming himself by a brazier when he heard footsteps. His main job was keeping out would-be thieves so he eased around the edge of the wheelhouse and looked along the wharf. A man in seaman's clothes was running towards the gangway. Behind him were three figures. They were dressed as ordinary seamen but their heads were straight out of a nightmare. One head was that of a stag, another a bear and the last a grotesque ape. Jim understood the frightened man's terror. Before the fleeing figure could reach the gangway one of the hunters seized him and threw him to the ground. The other started punching and kicking him as he lay helpless on the floor. Jim picked up a belaying pin and ran to the head of the gangway. The grotesques were so intent on beating their victim that for the moment they didn't see Jim. But the man on the floor did.

"Save me! For God's sake save me!" he screamed. The three men stopped and looked up to where Jim stood, baton raised but hesitating to put himself at risk. The bear-headed man gave his victim a final kick in the head and moved menacingly up the gangway towards Jim. Fear galvanised Jim into action, belaying pin swinging down in a wide arc. It was a lucky blow. Restricted by the sides of the gangway the bear-man had nowhere to go. He tried to duck under the striking arm but only managed to deflect the blow. It was enough to stun him. In a blind panic, Jim rushed down the gangway, arm raised and screaming. The two remaining ghouls saw him coming, aimed a couple more blows at the prone figure for luck then deliberately pushed him off the quayside into the water below. Jim decided it was more important to rescue the unconscious man than to try his luck with the monster-men. Before he could dive in he was seized and knocked to the ground. As he lay there in a daze he saw the third man rejoin them and they took off the rubber masks they were wearing. Jim felt relieved. At least he wasn't dealing with the supernatural. The men pulled him to his feet. Two of them were for knocking him on the head and sending him to join the man in the water below. The third objected. He said they had no quarrel with him and if he would give them his solemn word that he would never repeat what he saw they would let him go. Besides, the ship was due to sail in a few hours' time and if Jim didn't want to be left behind as a police witness he would keep *stumm* for his own sake. The others reluctantly agreed. Jim gave his word, the ship sailed and the mystery of Daniel's death would have remained a mystery if Jim hadn't developed a fever and blurted out the terrible story that had haunted him for the last 20 years of his life.

Tony questioned the old man about the time and date. The old man fumbled in his inside pocket and brought out a crumpled piece of paper and held it to the light of the fire so that he could read it: "December 24th 1857."

Tony sat back stunned. He had no doubt that Richard Trew's story was true. It fitted all the facts of the vision he had witnessed that Christmas Eve long ago. He questioned Trew to try and find out if he had any idea why the grotesquely masked men had been chasing his brother. Was it a simple mugging or was there something more sinister attached to the fright-masks. Trew didn't know. His son, when tackled on the subject shortly before his death, was of the opinion that the murder wasn't a simple mugging that had gone horribly wrong. He had the feeling that Daniel had known his assailants and what they intended to do with him. Buenos Aires was, at this time, one of the wildest towns in the world – at least in La Bocca, the port district that produced the tango and some of the most vicious knife fighters in the criminal underworld. How Daniel had managed to cross them remains a mystery. How Tony had shared those last horrific moments with his twin brother is an even greater mystery. It is not unknown for twins, miles apart, to share experiences but rarely, if ever, has the experience been so graphic and horrifying.

21
Lawrence

... shrieking forms in a circular desert
Weaving with contagion of putrescent embraces
On dissolving bone

T. S. Eliot *The Family Reunion*

DESERT WASTES. The only movement amongst the yellow, drifting sands and the sparse camel scrub is provided by the heat haze distorting the horizon. Then in the distance, swimming in the haze, appears a black dot. It wobbles, disintegrates and reforms as it comes straight towards the camera. The camera draws back slightly, shows the low, broken wall of a desert well. An Arab drinks, then notices the blob on the shimmering horizon. The black shape seems to detach itself from the sands but comes on remorselessly, growing more liquid as it gets nearer. A faint sound is picked up, a "sough-sough", rhythmic and growing louder all the time. Other sounds intrude. A jingle of harness and the rasp of heavy breathing. Now the figure detaches itself from the shifting background and can be seen for what it is. A man in Arab dress riding a camel. Still it comes on, gaining detail by the second. When it reaches the well the man reins in and pulls down his mask. Omar Sharif comes to a halt facing T.E. Lawrence – Lawrence of Arabia. Okay, it's not T.E. himself but the actor who has virtually become the Che Guevara of the sands – Peter O'Toole. It became one of the greatest scenes in a movie and overshadowed the rest of the story. It is the scene everyone remembers. Which is a shame because the Lawrence story is a great adventure story. Even his death was a thing of mystery.

Lawrence was the sort of individual who can grow up to be an obsessed trainspotter or an astronomer spending each waking night staring into the galaxy and getting excited about a speck of light he hasn't seen before. In short, he was obsessive. When he left university the thing that obsessed him was maps. He couldn't get enough of the fine detail. The discrepancies that crept onto the atlas, before the advent of the satellite and instruments more accurate than a lead weight on a piece of string and a wetted finger held up to the wind were a source of academic pleasure to him. His posting to Cairo on the outbreak of the First World War to try and bring some order to the trackless wastes of the desert was the catalyst that transformed him from an anorak into one of the sexiest heroes in history. The cartographical division came under the control of the Intelligence Department. It was a cushy number and most of the spies who should have been out getting their knees brown in the desert preferred to slake their not inconsiderable thirst in the wadis of Shepherds Hotel. Lawrence, as a newly arrived officer, was expected to join the gin and tonic brigade. Instead he fell in love with the desert.

The general attitude of his fellows was that the situation, viz the "wogs", was nothing to get excited about. After all they kept out of the way and if you kicked them hard enough you could even get them to press your number one uniform and polish the old jack-boots. Lawrence was appalled. He studied what information came into the office and made a point of questioning anyone who might be able to shed some light on what was going on beyond the portals of the Hotel. And who was doing what to whom. His sympathies were with the Arabs who were under the military thumb of Turkey. They tried to restore national pride by ill-advised forays against the invaders but without some sort of overall plan and an effort to stop the different desert tribes from trying to annihilate each other as a side issue, it was obvious that they were never going to get to first base, let alone score a home-run and remove the Turks from their land.

Lawrence began to take on more of the work, which gave him a chance to get out into the dunes. He got his information direct from the Arabs rather than filtered through the boredom-biased intelligence officers who rarely went beyond city limits and never talked to an Arab socially. His compatriots egged him on. They thought it was a great joke when Lawrence abandoned his peaked cap and started wearing a native *burnouse*. They even encouraged him. While he was out there getting the low-down on the low-life and writing up long reports, it looked as if the department was doing something. At last his reports were noticed by General Allenby. He saw a chance to strengthen the accord between the Egyptian and the British governments. So he called Lawrence in, didn't comment on the commissioned officer's choice of headgear and listened while he waxed lyrical about his friends in the sand dunes. Allenby appointed him as Special Liaison Officer, gave him a promotion and a legend was born.

Inevitably Lawrence made grandiose promises to the Arabs that his country wouldn't keep. Equally inevitably little men have been hacking at his exploits to prove that

he was a liar at best and a traitor at worst. In 1998 a documentary was broadcast, the main intent of which was to prove that he couldn't have done some of the forced marches across the desert he claimed. It was undertaken by a local without much interest, a fan of Lawrence with a fragile grasp on his own capabilities and a woman who continually claimed that her camel wasn't fast enough. When the ill-assorted trio found that they couldn't compete with the pace that Lawrence had maintained to strike the enemy by surprise, they decided it was impossible and that Lawrence was a liar and a charlatan. Never for a moment did they think that the fault might be with them. If Lawrence had made it to the present day he would have recognised the breed. Before he came out of the desert there was already a queue of little men waiting to kick him in the shins.

In disgust Lawrence handed in his Sam Browne and swagger stick and returned to England. As a penance he joined the RAF as A.C. Shaw and was happy to be just an anonymous figure in a blue uniform. It didn't last long. He was found out and had to leave the service. Lawrence was nothing if not resourceful and before long he was back in uniform with a new name and even deeper cover. A.C. Ross served in his lowly position as an "erk" until he was discharged in 1935. He was then 46 and a far different character from the man who has inspired the Arab nation to take on the Turks. He bought a little cottage in Clouds Hill in Dorset and there wrote his magnum opus, *The Seven Pillars of Wisdom*. Not an easy read but those who have persisted to the end assert that it is a great philosophical work. But then they would, wouldn't they?

One of Lawrence's great passions was his motorbike. A fiercesome Brough Superior, voted by devotees as the best bit of two-wheel machinery assembled anywhere – ever! Although Lawrence wanted anonymity, it didn't mean that he abandoned all his friends. He was a regular guest at the homes of those he could trust. Winston

Churchill, in spite of some reservations about the worth of Lawrence's desert adventure, remained loyal. As did master wordsmith George Bernard Shaw. It was after dinner at Shaw's house that Lawrence made the transition from man to ghost. Riding his Brough Superior along a country lane he lost control and crashed out of this life and into the hereafter. Stories that others with an axe to grind were involved have largely been discounted although there are still conspiracy nuts who blame his death on anything from the Arabs who felt deserted to UFOs interested in his Brough Superior. Whatever the truth of the matter, Lawrence of Arabia was dead and soon buried – but not forgotten.

Within a few weeks there were reports that Lawrence had been seen either at his Clouds Hill cottage or riding his bike along the lane where he died. His executors, maybe expecting Lawrence to return and claim his property back, decided that the cottage should be left exactly as it had been when he went to that fatal dinner.

In death Lawrence has taken on the mantle shared by King Arthur and Sir Francis Drake. Like them he is expected to return and smite the enemy hip and thigh when England is in danger. This is because, it is alleged, there were many sightings of his ghost in the days leading up to the Second World War. Most people privileged to see the apparition report that he still wears the Arab costume of the desert. Probably this is because it was riding the sand dunes that brought him the most happiness. On the other hand it might be that he is wearing the usual ghostly apparel of a shroud and, because of the desert associations, those who see him assume he wears a *djallabiah*.

Most sightings report that he enters the gate to the Clouds Hill cottage and walks slowly and pensively to the front door and disappears inside. On the occasions when the watcher had the balls to follow him in, the cottage was discovered to be empty.

At the side of the lane is a little plaque commemorating the moment when Lawrence lost control, in whatever circumstances and for whatever reason, and crashed. It is a relatively quiet road and there have been many reports of the sound of a high-powered engine, roaring around the bend. Nothing appears to account for the sound. Other reports say that not only is there the sound of the motorbike but also the screech of brakes and the sounds of the crash itself. There are even those who claim to have seen him in the neighbourhood wearing his RAF uniform.

Why would Lawrence's shadow return to haunt his little cottage in Dorset? It is usually assumed that ghosts put in appearances where they had the most trauma in their life. That would mean that Lawrence should be wandering around the wadis and dunes of Egypt, blowing up a railway line here, raiding a Turkish army post there or maybe leading his colourful crew into Damascus. Unfortunately no reports have come from the desert so it must be assumed, from the fact that he appears at his cottage in Arab attire, that there is nothing for the desert guerilla in the sandy wastes.

It doesn't matter really. The monument of David Lean's film, *Lawrence of Arabia*, will keep him riding the desert ranges as long as there is a projector working or the memory of Sharif's epic ride into shot persists.

22
Princess Diana

Ha! while I gaze, pale Cynthia fades,
The bursting Earth unveils the Shades!

Thomas Parnell *A Night Piece on Death*

PRINCESS DIANA, of hallowed memory, hasn't made it into the ghostographers lexicon of famous apparitions yet but already there are reports from people walking in the vicinity of Pont de l'Alma of a ghostly car. At the moment it is unseen. A sound. The rush of a car travelling at high speed, the squeal of brakes followed by a tremendous crash. No sightings of spectral figures walking around the tunnel, no phantom Mercedes, lights ablaze, hurtling along the narrow lane. But they'll come. Too much grief and emotion is vested in the memory of lovely Diana for her just to fade away and become a name on a tub of margarine or a dusty Versace frock hanging in a trophy case. As a symbol of hope and understanding she was unparalleled. Even the sainted Mother Theresa couldn't claim the sort of affection that Diana commanded effortlessly. Apparently effortlessly. The turmoil of her private life suggests that her public persona was anything but untroubled. There is, of course, a major problem for the ghost of Diana. She was so much to so many people, each of whom have their own idea of what she was all about, that it is almost impossible to guess what the sightings of her troubled soul will be like. Will she be the young, slightly plump and wholly innocent Sloane Ranger? Or the tough international campaigner of the body armour and minefields? Dressed to kill in the deadly little black number she wore to put it to her weak-kneed husband on the night when Prince Charles publicly admitted his adultery in his landmark Dimbleby documentary or the exploded meringue of her wedding dress. It may sound facetious to talk about a public idol like this but like Jack Kennedy and Marilyn Monroe, she is heading for the sort of industry that has grown up around their deaths. In many ways Diana's claim to universal iconagraphical status is far greater than either Kennedy or Monroe. She has a family tree and history that reaches back through the centuries to the very moment when England stopped being composed of gangs of bovver boys with long hair, a bizarre dress code and a desire to bash anything that came within compass of their striking arm. On the other hand that sounds like a fairly reasonable description of the fans who flock to international football matches. Never mind. Let's just say that the very English Spencer family goes back a very long way. And have a ready-made anthology of hauntings. The ancestral home of the Spencer family at Althrop Park provides just the ambience that any restless aristocratic spirit would fit right into. Candidates for the earthly predecessor of the spirit girl who walks the corridors is uncertain. Even the well-heeled weren't safe from the old guy with the toothy grin and the scythe. Reaching the age of 21 was reckoned to be cause for throwing away the corks and getting into a full-blown orgy. What childbirth didn't glean, smallpox, scarlet fever, meningitis, diphtheria, pneumonia, tuberculosis and good old-fashioned neglect took care of. A high percentage of the infants born to a family never had the chance of making it through to an age when cancer and heart disease could finish them off.

Along with the usual white ladies, hooded monks, mysterious rappings and off-stage moaning, the Spencers have a couple of ghosts that have been attested to by persons of worth.

One is the shade of a little girl, about ten years old, who was seen on a number of occasions around the turn of the century, eighteenth to nineteenth, that is, not the new one hovering on the brink of a maladjusted microchip. The girl was wearing the type of suffocating clothes that was tight, right and proper for young ladies of class and breeding in the mid-1800s. She was seen and described by one of the young Spencer girls. As far as we know this was not, *per se*, a cry for attention, although since the original witness left the Spencer fold sightings of the ethereal playmate have been exceedingly few and extraordinarily far between.

Another ghost that has a short CV of hauntings was spotted some time before the little girl was even born – if her reported clothes are any indication of era. Again the story comes from around the turn of the century – seventeenth to eighteenth in this case. The Spencer family must be extra-sensitive to turns of centuries. Perhaps the Diana sightings have yet to find their time?

The story goes that a certain clergyman called Drury was a guest in the house. He was game for a lark and after feeding at the Spencer table and beating Lord Littleton, husband of one of the ubiquitous Spencer girls, at billiards, he retired with a bottle of brandy to his austere four-poster bed with the duck-feather-filled mattress, made his usual mumbled obeisances to God before crashing out, fully clothed, on top of the blankets. Next thing he knew was that someone was hovering over him with a bright light. At first seized with the fear that this might be the much vaunted light that led departing souls into the afterlife he was only a little consoled to make out the form of a man in a flat hat and a striped nightshirt standing by the side of the bed holding a lamp. To hide his initial fright, the good reverend swore heartily at the intruder and told him to be gone in slightly unclerical terms. The man held frame for a second or two before turning and walking into the dressing room. Drury didn't seem to think this strange. The original fright from the rude awakening had receded taking the overdose of adrenalin it had released with it. Now the bubbles of alcohol flooded back and he flopped on the pillow and fell instantly into a dead sleep.

Next morning was not good. The hangover made him truculent and he wanted to hand out a little of the pain he was getting as his brain tried to claw a way through his eye sockets and his stomach threatened to cover Northamptonshire in ordure. His lordship not being available, Drury unloaded on Lady Littleton and demanded that the servant who had so disgracefully interrupted his God-given slumbers should be sacked immediately. Adroitly her ladyship defended her position. What Reverend Drury had seen was, in fact, the ghost of her father's number one groom. Her father, George John Spencer, the second Earl, had been terrified of fire. It hadn't stopped him from living a full and happy life. His fear did not extend to his getting a personal invitation from Old Nick to join him in the Other Place. Just to make sure that his exodus to the hotter place wasn't preceded by a grilling in this, he instructed the groom to check up on his guests, who were not always too lucid by the time they got to bed, and make sure they hadn't left a burning candle by a hanging drapery or nodded off with a cigar in their mouth. It was a reasonable explanation but Drury's migraine was threatening to detonate his eyeballs and he wasn't going to be appeased that easily. But Lady Littleton had a capper that stopped him pursuing the subject further. The groom had finally hung up his spurs and departed to a better life a fortnight earlier. What Drury must have seen was the groom's ghost. The perfect retainer, carrying on his duties in the face of what most employers would have thought were reasonable circumstances for a night off.

A more affable ghost has clearly been identified as that of Edward John Spencer, grandfather of the Princess of Wales and the seventh Earl to bear the Spencer name. In ghost terms Edward is a new boy. He only negotiated the great divide in 1975 but was soon popping up at parties and family reunions. Shortly after his death, at a party thrown by his son, the eighth Earl Johnny Spencer and his new wife Raine, he was seen circulating amongst the guests, generally appearing to enjoy himself. At other times he is known to waft around the house being avuncular and pleasantly smiling to anyone who comes within sight of his manifestation. He looks so solid and friendly that several people have been known to address him as if he was still pumping blood through his veins. There is a degree of interactivity between those seeing him and the echo of the seventh Earl. The housekeeper, who has seen him on a number of occasions, swears he smiles at her when she addresses him. A workman, who didn't know who he was, claims to have been the inspiration for a spiritual nod from the wraith.

So will Lady Diana decide to return to her roots and haunt the manor? Will she choose the wedding dress for her spectral visitation? If ever a dress was suitable for the afterlife, that particular Emmanuel dress is. It was the focus of billions of eyes the first time out and covered the tears and humiliation of a virginal bride who was already aware that the vows being taken were no more than a ritual. Vows that in their solemnity and depth appeared to be immutable but were, in a few short years, to be disclaimed by some of the Lords of the Church to be something said on the spur of the moment and to have no validity when adults, particularly, Royal adults, wanted to forget them.

Yes! Diana, with her well-known appreciation of what makes a telling PR statement would definitely opt for the wedding dress. Unfortunately the bridal gown is only suitable for Althrop Hall or St Paul's Cathedral. This rather argues for a reenactment of the car crash at the Pont de l'Alma. Splendidly theatrical, this is one ghostly venue that she would do well to miss – although whether the French tourist guides will be able to do the same is another *chose*.

The other site could be the minefields of Angola. An arresting image in a fraught situation. But who will be there to bear witness? Every possible venue has its inherent faults but there is one thing for certain. If there was ever a lady who knew how to work a situation to her advantage, that lady was Diana, Princess of Wales. So we'll just have to wait and see what the turn of the century brings ...

23
Nell Gwyn

Thus the damsel spake, and died.

Thomas Chatterton *Song From Aella*

NOT SURPRISING FOR a woman who walked the streets of London enticing men to buy her oranges and finished up as the favourite courtesan of the King of England, the ghost of Nell Gwyn, or more formally, Eleanor Gwyn, pops up in palaces, manorial halls and theatres throughout the land. Nell's parents lived in the Covent Garden area. She hardly knew her father; he was a travelling man and after Nell's mum, Helena, told him she was in the pudding club he upped and travelled. It didn't do him much good. He was arrested for fraud in Oxford and banged up in a debtors' prison. A travelling man cooped up in a cell doesn't last long and Nell's father died. Helena had been a prostitute in her youth but managed to acquire a bob or two once her husband left and set herself up in a "caff". The general clientele consisted of foreigners, petty crooks, market traders, pimps and prostitutes. Nell grew up short-changing the customers and fending off inquisitive hands with wit, good humour and a kick in the testicles. She had a sister called Rosie who had a share of a concession in the Kings Theatre and parcelled a piece out to Nell when their mother's liver exploded. Nell saw the erotic possibilities of an orange and founded her fame on a citrus fruit. Before long she was up on the stage, courted by gentry and royalty. Increasing fame brought increasingly wealthy patrons until she became the prime pastime of Charles II and the

only mistress who was acceptable to the King's subjects – mainly because she kept her cockney accent and could swear like a Billingsgate porter. She also had a remarkable capacity for spending money and, in spite of never being off the stage and being treated generously by Charles, she was always in debt. It got so bad in the end that, if she went out alone, she went in disguise.

Then what could have ruined any chance of a comfortable old age occurred. Above her *décolleté* in debt, with only the King between her and the debtor's jail that had finished off her father, she heard that Charles was on his death bed. She need not have worried. Charles was a man who didn't mind paying for his fun so he clutched his brother's hand and uttered the immortal words to the soon-to-be James II, "Let not poor Nell starve ..." before the death rattle and the mandatory white light cut short any further communication. James II might not have been everybody's cup of tea but he did right by Nell. He paid off her debts and put her on a pension of £1.50 per annum, a not inconsiderable sum in 1685. In the long run it didn't cost as much as it might. Two years later, at the age of thirty-seven, the divine Nell had a stroke and died. And so began the hauntings.

Salisbury Hall was the home of Winston Churchill's mother Jenny who, after Winnie's father Randolph died of syphilis, brought her new husband, obviously a courageous man, to live in the house. It had a chequered

history. One of the occupants, although his name had never appeared on the rent book, was Charles II. He bought the house through an intermediary for Nell. Soon after Jennie became Mrs Cornwallis-West, she moved in with husband George who reported seeing a young and beautiful woman on the stairs. Not wishing to miss out on what might be an opportunity *en maison*, he followed her. She went round a corner and, wouldn't you know it, disappeared. George discreetly asked around and was told that what he had seen wasn't some chambermaid who might be up for some rumpy-pumpy and a half crown to keep her mouth shut, but the spirit of Nell Gwyn, no less. Nell has also been known to appear in theatres, normally on first nights and always in a merry mood. Her laughter and scampering feet have been heard in all sorts of buildings and public places. The fact that it was Nell Gwyn, or E.G. as she liked to be known around the city, has been attested by some sober people and many drunken actors. How you identify a long-lost laugh and the scamper of fleeing feet is best not enquired into too closely.

Nell was buried at her own request in St Martin in the Fields in London. Although it is not accorded the status of one of her more authorised hauntings it was here in 1968 that a Japanese woman claimed to have been confronted by a woman, slender, pretty etc, wearing a full skirt and low-cut blouse, who appeared to be looking up the road as if expecting someone. The Japanese lady seized the opportunity to ask her the way to Buckingham Palace. The beautiful lady smiled and told her that she was Nell Gwyn and promptly vanished. The Japanese lady assumed that in the ancient city of London it was quite normal for ladies to say their name and vanish. Back in Japan she mentioned the encounter to a friend who told it to another friend, who told it to a journalist who told it to everyone. The lady is now famous as the Lotus Blossom who met Nell Gwyn.

Nell Gwyn was a colourful character with a multitude of high-profile lovers and a theatre CV that could hardly be bettered by any leading lady since. It is surprising that more movies haven't been made about her. My favourite, although only a "who'll-buy-my-oranges" part, was in the 40s film with Sid Field – *Cardbox Cavalier*. She also featured in *Forever Amber* but it was hardly a "part".

24
Witchfinder

The Puritan through life's sweet garden goes
To pluck the thorn and cast away the rose

Kenneth Hare

I N THE 17TH CENTURY the trade, occupation or vocation of Witchfinder General was a calling of which any right-minded mother with a religion fixation could be justly proud. It wasn't a particularly difficult job. Basically all you needed were a pair of buckle shoes, a tall hat and a well-starched, wide white collar and you were in business. It also helped if you had a friend in high ecclesiastical circles in case you pulled a wrong-un and burned somebody who also had connections. Then it was a case of your connections being better than those of the burned. What better role model could anyone have than Peter Cushing. As Gustav Weil in *Twins of Evil* (1971), he virtually fashioned the mould for over-zealous, over-sexed and over the centuries puritanical censors. With a little help from Vincent Price, whose obsessed, evil-finger-pointing *Witchfinder General* (1968) set a new standard in violence and a new slant on Christianity without the restraining influence of Jesus. The Witchfinder General was a down-market Protestant answer to the Grand Inquisitor of the Catholic Church. The GI was into full burning and butchering in the twelfth and thirteenth centuries. The Witchfinder General didn't don buckles and stiff white collar until the age of puritanical excess, which began in the early seventeenth century.

Basically the Inquisitor and Witchfinder worked to the same agenda. Move into a district, stir up a bit of local hysteria, get everybody telling tales on their neighbours, family and friends to protect themselves, demand confessions that made very little difference to the ultimate sentence, and then burn anybody whose name pops up in the tribunal. Arthur Miller's *The Crucible* gives a very graphic and moody indication of what happened when someone started pointing the bone in Salem, Massachussetts in the spring of 1692. At this time America was still largely a conclave of disaffected Brits looking for an identity in a country bigger and more varied than the ideals they had left the old one to pursue. One method of extracting the "truth" as the Witchfinder saw it was very efficacious in Salem. Find someone who had nothing to confess but who had upset his neighbour in some way, thereby having a reliable witness to all sorts of erotic devilling, stick him between a couple of boards, like ham in a sandwich, pile boulders on him until bones begin to break and breathing becomes impossible and what have you got? A miscreant who will embellish the Witchfinder General's clear-up rate by as much as his malicious questioner wants answers to. It was very much *en vogue* in England at this time and the American practitioners of the art of persuasion were probably encouraged by the case of one of his Old World predecessors, Witchfinder General Matthew Hopkins.

Hopkins was a man of many talents. He wasn't restricted to the stone-press and the purifying flames. One very effective way of getting to the truth was to stretch the accused backwards over a horizontal pole and hang weights on his feet and around his neck until his back snapped or he choked to death – preferably after he had told Hopkins what he wanted to know and blessed him for helping to research and display the relative part of his faulty memory. Hopkins was also extraordinarily fond of the ducking stool. Everybody knows how this works. You pick a likely heretic, usually female of haglike appearance or buxom and not willing to put out for whoever denounced her, and march her to the obligatory idyllic village pond. There you stripped her off, pressed the kids' see-saw into religious duty and placed it by the side of the pond. Next the hag or buxom wench is tied to one end and a couple of beefy lads from the village stationed at the other. Hopkins then put the question to those in danger of losing their immortal souls and stood politely back while they considered the answer that might get them back to their hovel, relatively unscathed, in the shortest possible time. As this question was on a level of "Have you stopped beating your husband?" the answer tended to incriminate rather than absolve. Hopkins could afford to wait. It heightened the drama and built tension amongst the audience. All the villagers were forced to watch. This guaranteed that any waverer's memories would be prompted and they would bear witness and help drive Satan from their community. For those perched on the stool this was supposed to be the time when recanting could suck them back into the fold. In reality anything they said would be dismissed as the outpourings of a circumscribed soul.

Hopkins then gave a little job talk, letting everyone know that if he let anyone tainted by Satan escape it would be more than his job's worth and laid down the general principles of what was about to happen – viz the accused would be lowered into the water by the lusty lads. If she (it was usually a she, medieval PC not being something to preoccupy the normal conscience) sank – all well and good. She might be dead but at least she died in a state of grace. If she floated it proved she was a witch and could safely be hauled off to the stake and incinerated. That normally did the job – fire, as always, purifies. It was truly amazing how few were proved innocent by the ducking stool.

When Matthew Hopkins turned up in Misley, a short distance from the ancient Roman town of Colchester in the summer of 1647, he thought it was going to be business as usual. Essex was a great burning-at-the-stake county, right up until the nineteenth century. In the seventeenth century there were more flambéed peasantry than they had had hot dinners. A few too many. It had become almost a county ritual since Boadicea had torched Colchester in Roman times. The villagers stood around muttering rhubarb but when Hopkins seized on one of the more fanciable maidens, who had promised favours to half the hot-bloods in lust, it was too much. They watched as the girl was humiliated and accused of all sorts of unnatural practices without making a move but then Hopkins made an untypical miscalculation. When he stripped off the girl and paraded her amongst her peers to humiliate her she looked so sexy that all the men under 80, and probably a few over, rose as one, grabbed Hopkins and beat him senseless. It felt so good they wanted more. After years of trembling in fear at the mention of the name of the man from the puritanical society it was great to feel the snap of a bone under a well-directed boot. It wasn't enough. Once the blood-lust is flowing, nothing is. They stripped off Hopkins' buckled shoes and Puritan collar, dragged him naked around the green before tying him semiconscious to the notorious ducking stool. It was a great gag and, of course, they all felt terribly disappointed when they found out that Hopkins had told those who had preceded him in the ducking stool the truth. The liberation of his true spirit was so traumatic that it is now bound to the place of his departure and many villagers have testified to his runty figure wandering around the area of Mistley as if he is looking for something. Probably still can't believe that the locals can be so insensitive to his divine mission.

25
Dona Leonora Oviedo

Though lovers be lost love shall not;
And death shall have no dominion.

Dylan Thomas

MOST HAUNTINGS CAN be pretty naff. A misty figure in a transparent sheet skulking around doing the "whoo whoo" bit and frightening everyone out of their clogs. Always just out of focus or disappearing as soon as they are approached. Occasionally something more exotic comes along or, more properly, hangs about.

Take the Green Lady who puts herself about at Thorpe Hall in Lincolnshire. She quite blatantly wants to be seen and haunts not only the house but the gardens as well. It's that good old plot standby that keeps her earthbound and determined not to be overlooked in the afterlife. Ladies who lurk usually forget any sartorial sense they might have had in life and are content to waft about in the shadows clad in virginal white or not-sure grey. Our Lady of Thorpe Hall opts for a rather splendid green. And she has a story that is just as colourful.

Back in 1596 when Britain was beginning to flirt with the idea that by ruling the waves they could rule the world and Raleigh was in Cadiz singeing the King of Spain's beard, Doña Leonora Oviedo met and fell in love with John Bolle, the owner of Thorpe Hall. He had put a considerable amount of cash into Raleigh's enterprise and wanted to share in the spoils. Spoils came in all shapes and sizes and for Bolle, Leonora fitted into most categories. Before long they were an item and, when

Bolle waxed lyrical after coitus, Leonora listened intently. She liked what she heard. Bolle obviously had a bob or two and wasn't afraid to spend it. He told her about the house he was having built, which he intended to call Thorpe Hall. He spoke so much about Thorpe Hall that Leonora thought he was trying to sell her the concept of living there. It didn't take her long to decide that she wouldn't mind exchanging the hot dusty days and mosquito-fraught nights for a go at being lady of the manor in England's green and pleasant land. John Bolle either didn't notice her "our" when she was talking about Thorpe Hall or let it ride, safe in the knowledge that when the call came to board ship, as a friend of Sir Francis he would be first aboard and the gangway would be whipped away smartish if Doña Leonora tried to follow. So he didn't discourage her misty eyed pleas for the future and continued to have his feet firmly planted under her duvet.

The day came when Raleigh was fed up with lolling around on the headland waiting for some prize merchant ship to blunder into his path and decided to go back to England, flirt with Elizabeth and use her connections to line up a gaggle of investors for some new venture. The elusive North West passage seemed a likely winner. Who could resist the chance of pouring gold into an enterprise that promised to open up a new and quicker route to the

Orient and change curry into currency? John Bolle was equal to the task and gave Doña Leonora a sailor's farewell. It had been fun while it lasted but he had no intention of returning to England with a dago aristo in tow. Some things you just didn't do. Especially if you wanted to be a bowing and scraping part of the Tudor court. His protestation that their separation would be only for a short time and that he would return, marry and take her away from all this sounded a bit hollow even in his own ears but he mustered enough emotion to convince his Spanish lady that he was devastated by Raleigh's decision to return to England. *Que lastima*, there wasn't even time for them to get married.

A portrait had been painted of Leonora in a green dress during the time that Bolle had come a-courting. He professed to be enraptured by the portrayal of her dark beauty and, this being a time before the Happy Snap had been invented, Leonora insisted that her lover took with him the huge, gold-framed painting.

Back in Thorpe Hall, Bolle found a blank wall and stuck the picture up in a prominent place. It was a good conversation piece and made him look like a bit of a swashbuckling ladies' man. He didn't forget her – how could he with her picture dominating the hall – but he had no intention of ever returning to her neck of the isthmus again. Doña Leonora began to get the idea that she had been given the long farewell as the months passed and she heard nothing from her British sea-dog. She was dismayed but understanding. It was quite obvious that something catastrophic had happened to keep him from her and it was up to her to seize the initiative and go to him. Once her mind was made up she packed her *maletas*, making sure the green dress she had worn for the portrait was properly stored, took a coach to France and then boarded ship for England.

You can imagine John Bolle's surprise when she rolled up the drive at Thorpe Hall. He covered well and gave her all the old guff about it being wonderful to see her before whisking her up to the bedroom to sample some of the Spanish fruits he had enjoyed so much in their home country. Before he had finished his after-sex clay-pipe of the newly imported tobacco, he was laying down a scheme to dump the exciting but decidedly non-British bit of totty he had hoped he had lost forever. At first Leonora affected not to notice but spent her spare time roaming around the magnificent hall and gardens kidding herself that some day she would be the mistress of all she surveyed. She began to get the feeling that she wasn't wanted when her erstwhile lover kept asking when she would be going home and dropping hints about boats leaving for the Continent. She managed to ignore the hints for a long time but then Bolle got involved in another enterprise and told her he was shutting up the Hall and offered to get her a one-way on the evening tide. This was too much for the hot-blooded Spaniard and she threatened to kill herself. John was polite but explained that, as much as he would love to spend the rest of eternity with her, when duty called there was nothing a true blue, seafaring dog of an Englishman could do but obey. Just to show how romantic and distraught he was at their parting he suggested a last dinner. A chance to indulge the heart-wrenching sorrow of their imminent parting. Again Doña Leonora warned that she wouldn't be there for him to make a fool of again and ran into the garden. Bolle felt positively relieved. At least he had got the principle across that they were not to be joined permanently at the hip. Who knows? In a year or two, if he was down Cadiz way, they might get together in the back room for another rumbustious communion. It was with a light heart and a sense of wellbeing that he ordered the table laid for two and the nearest thing the cook could come to *empanadas* as a starter.

Out in the garden Doña Leonora Oviedo was having

an emotional crisis. She had hoped that the threat to do herself an injury might have had enough effect on her cold lover to galvanise him into following her into the garden. When he didn't come a-running, or even at a casual saunter, she was forced to move to plan B. It wasn't what she wanted but, naively, she expected it to be instantly efficacious. She took out the sharp little dagger she carried tucked in her skirt to ward off any pickpockets who might decide that a lady of foreign extraction might be up for an easy mugging and, after just one more glance back at the house to see if her paramour was coming, she slit her wrists. Unfortunately her timing wasn't good. Before she could stagger, bloodstained but not in immediate danger of dying, into the dining room where Bolle was waiting, she died.

Bolle eschewed the *empanadas* and tucked into the rack of beef when she didn't turn up. He thought it was all terribly bad form but what more could you expect from a dago and a woman at that. Replete, he went to bed. He was only slightly peeved when his butler woke him up in the morning with the news that her ladyship's body had been found, white and still, amongst the rhubarb in the kitchen garden.

It came as a bit of a shock to the owner of Thorpe Hall. A house guest ending up a corpse in the kitchen garden was bad form. Luckily nobody outside his immediate household knew about his amorous guest and he meant to keep it that way. He arranged a discreet funeral in the grounds but was unable to find a Catholic priest to conduct the service. Catholic priests, like Spanish grandees, were not acceptable society in England during the sixteenth and seventeenth centuries. Rather than call

attention to the passing of his ex-lover, Bolle mumbled a few words over her grave, warned his servants of what would happen to them if they so much as thought of his recent guest, and went back to the happy life of a country squire. Just to show how romantically inclined he was he ordered that a place should be set each evening for his missing guest – a custom that was carried out nightly until the guilt for what had happened to the Lady in Green had been expiated in the 1920s.

Whatever sop Bolle had thought he was tossing to fate by hanging Leonora's picture on the wall and laying her place at dinner was not enough to keep Leonora quietly interred in the garden with her bones. Before long reports were being filed of the tragic Lady in Green rushing around the manor house and drifting through the rhododendrons in the grounds. It wasn't hard to figure out what had made her a restless spirit in the old tradition. Unrequited love, love-sickness, suicide and the ultimate humiliation of being buried like a dog in the rhododendrons without a priest of her faith to give her a proper send-off and introduction into the hereafter. Then there was the constant psychic focal point of the picture and ritual plate-playing. Headstrong and naive she may have been but she didn't deserve to be buried in an unmarked grave and that alone would be enough for some restless spirits. John Bolle never told anyone the location of the last resting place of Doña Leonora so until some kind soul with a sharp shovel, a sense of psychic decency and a strong back comes along and starts digging in the grounds of Thorpe Hall the ghost of the Lady in Green will continue to be a talking point for daytrippers on a visit.

26
Trains and Boats and Planes

O, for an engine to keep back all clocks!

Ben Jonson

TRAINS, PROBABLY BECAUSE they were big in the hey-day of apparitions, the late Victorian era, have more than their fair share of sightings. Phantom trains have been seen on all the main lines and quite a few of the small off-shoots. Once again the west country can claim more than an average share of the hauntings. At Blue Anchor, half a dozen miles from the Butlins town of Minehead, there's a ghostly porter. He got that way through carelessness and still doesn't seem to realise that he has gone before. It seems that he returned from an ample dinner late one night to pass on the key, or whatever it's called, to the train travelling from Watchet in the east to Minehead in the west. It was essential that the train had the key because it signalled that the line ahead was clear. On a single track line it can be embarrassing to come across another engine travelling in the opposite direction. There was also the gate across the level crossing. This was years before the new-fangled remote-controlled devices had been installed, and it meant getting your back into it and pushing open the barrier yourself. There was a little confusion. The porter handed over the key, exchanged a few playful unpleasantries with the engine driver and went to open the gate. Somehow, between pushing open the gate and juggling the heavy carbide lamp that was used for signalling the all clear, things began to go wrong. Whatever happened, the train started off

prematurely. The porter had laid one gate back and was halfway through opening the second when the engine took him unawares and killed him on the spot. Since that long ago accident many a man crossing the track late at night has heard the plaintive whistle from the steam engine and seen the ghostly outline of the porter struggling to open the heavy gates, unaware of either the menace of the approaching train or that his last drama was enacted and concluded many years ago.

Four or five miles away was the old Mineral Line. This runs from the tiny seaport of Watchet into the Brendon Hills and terminates at a gothic winding station on top of a steep hill up which empty trains would be dragged by steam winch and steel hawsers to the loading bay. Through Washford, the stop on the line after Watchet, it passes behind ancient Cleve Abbey, which was one of the houses that Henry VIII knocked about a bit during the Reformation. At Roadwater, another couple of miles along the track, the station house has been converted into a bungalow and submerged in the workers' cottages and weekend haunts for city folk that have proliferated since the line became defunct in March 1861. Rayleigh Cross was where the main mines were sunk and for, a brief period in the latter half of the nineteenth century, the men and women who hacked the tin from the deep pits brought some sort of prosperity to the area. Then some clever accountant decided that it would be more economical to close the mines and import tin ore from Spain and Portugal. Result – derelict houses, an old tin church, dangerous, collapsing mine shafts and a mass of people, brought in from not only the far-flung corners of Britain but also from the Continent, unemployed. All this woe didn't go unnoticed on the astral plane and to this day there are decaying signal boxes that come to life at certain times, the wail of a late night train chugging through the little villages *en route* and fuzzy figures signalling trains as they go through Roadwater.

The worst hauntings, however, come from a point between Watchet and Washford called Kentsford. The motivating force for the line that ripped through the beautiful valley, named by the Romans as the Valley of Flowers, was greed. Fat men in stovepipe hats believed that if they didn't strip the mineral wealth from the hills there would be another busload along in a minute with plenty of entrepreneurs who would.

To maximize output they brought in the trains as soon as the line was laid. This meant that everything was done on the nod and nobody really knew what was happening. And, of course, it also meant that work on the line was still going on when the trains started rolling. It was inevitable that there should be a grand cock-up and in August 1859 it came. A loaded train was on its way to Watchet harbour when it met an unloaded train making its way up the valley. No proper signalling or advanced warning system had been installed and there was so much confusion that nobody noticed a minor incident like two opposing engines going flat out in opposite directions on a single track! The result was catastrophic. Engines and trains went careening off at every angle taking track workers and onlookers with it. Body count was three dead and dozens seriously hurt. The owners of the railway were terribly upset. Operations had to be suspended for over a week while the track was relaid and the engines recovered. It was also terribly inconvenient

that so many of the workers had been marginalised. It took time to collect a gang of workers in such an out-of-the-way place. And time is money!

Maybe those who were killed didn't quite see it that way. Time was what they didn't have – in this life at least. So they took time into their own hands and now, when the conditions are right for a good haunting, the sound of the two trains heading inexorably towards each other, the screech of steel against steel as the drivers apply the brakes in a desperate effort to avoid disaster and the yells and screams of the men as the loaded trucks skip the rails and ploughs them under, can be heard.

At the other end of the country, or is that the UK to be politically correct, in Edinburgh, a railway haunting of a very different nature took place quite recently. Maybe haunting is the wrong description. This was more in the nature of a timeslip. Whatever, it happened to an actress and she swears it is true.

Jennifer Croxton had been in Edinburgh for a couple of days working on a television show. She was pretty exhausted and the weather was particularly foul, so as soon as she got an opportunity to leave, she grabbed it with both hands and headed for the station. It was in the days before private enterprise dictated that commuting between Britain's major cities, trainwise, should cease around dinner time. She was just in time to scramble aboard as doors began to slam and porters became hostile. By the time she had sorted herself out and looked around she was amazed to see that she was in one of the old fashioned corridor trains with compartments leading off and dim lamps that, in retrospect, she thinks were probably gas. She was more than happy when she edged along the corridor to see that the compartments were obviously first class with wide comfortable armchair like seats instead of the plastic utilitarian jobs most trains have now. One of the first compartments had only an old lady sitting in it reading. Jennifer opened the door, heaved her bag onto the rack above the seat and dropped into the far corner. The other passenger didn't even look up. Jennifer wasn't particularly frazzled. All she wanted to do was get the six-hour journey behind her and climb into her own bed. She leafed through the magazines she had bought but nothing caught her attention so she put them on the seat beside her and studied the old lady in the corner who continued to read without acknowledging her presence. She was dressed in shiny materials of black and mauve. The dress had a full skirt and a high waist. The top was a short, decorated jacket of sorts, high at the neck and wide of shoulder. Jennifer couldn't see her face too well. The light, what light there was, illuminated the book but kept her features in the shadow. The dress was odd but, in the modern world where body and face piercing are almost accepted as the norm and you can see anything from green top hats and velvet overcoats to cloche hats and folderols on the streets, what does "a little old-fashioned" mean?

Jennifer also noticed for the first time how cold it was in the cabin. She had worked up a bit of a sweat catching the train and hadn't noticed at first. She pulled her coat around her and looked around for the source of the coldness. Opposite, above the back of the winged seats, was a temperature control. It was a simple pointer on a pivot written around it was "Full – Medium – Cold". The pointer was resting on "Full". Jennifer sat looking at it for a while, trying to figure out why the compartment was cold when it should be at least warm. Finally she got up, apologised to the old lady and jiggled the control from side to side. The old lady took no notice. Jennifer slumped back in her seat and tried to convince herself that she was getting warmer. When she lost contact with her feet she had to confess that she was fooling herself. The silent passenger continued to read her book and take no notice at all of Jennifer humping and shifting. She

came to the conclusion that she had to move before frostbite set in. Find a guard, a restaurant car or even a warm loo. She debated with herself whether or not she should take her bag. She felt a bit embarrassed. Maybe the old lady would take it as a slight if she left the carriage. By now Jennifer didn't care. She had to get warm. She grabbed her bag, mumbled some weak excuse, which even she couldn't understand, and left the carriage. She decided to look for a restaurant car. Some hope, but she was nothing if not optimistic. She pushed open the door at the end of the corridor and stepped through. It was like going into another world. Bright neon lights illuminated the tatty plastic and nylon seats and men and women were sprawled around in grotesque positions trying to get some sleep. For a moment Jennifer considered going back to her seat but she remembered the cold and decided anything was better than that. Anyway, it was only one carriage. Maybe further forward things would be better. They weren't. Nor did there seem to be a restaurant car. A guard, who happened to come from the opposite direction confirmed this but said that there was a buffet car in carriage G. It was better than nothing. As she pushed past him, more for something to say to avoid the embarrassment of close contact with a stranger than any expectation of finding a solution, she mentioned the fact that the heating appeared to be of the non-functioning variety in the first-class compartment. He looked at her in surprise and said that he had just come from there and no-one had complained. The way he said it Jennifer understood him to mean that he had come from a first-class carriage at the front of the train. She carefully explained that she was talking about the compartment at the *rear* of the train. The guard had been up to his neck in complaining passengers and didn't want to get into some pointless argument with a confused female passenger.

"There are no first-class compartments in the rear!" he

snapped and passed on. Annoyed, Jennifer turned and stomped off to carriage G, which was as ghastly as any other buffet car that anyone has ever been in. While she sipped some warmth back into her body with a double brandy she thought about what the guard had said and got steadily more belligerent as she remembered the rude way he had dismissed her. She downed another swift one, gathered up her bag and marched off down the train, determined to teach the guard a lesson. There she ran into a problem. In spite of walking the length of the train countless times she couldn't find that old-fashioned compartment with the old-fashioned lady.

27
Panic

I moan in sleep when I hear afar their whirling laughter.

James Joyce *I Hear an Army Charging Upon the Land*

IT HAS OFTEN been said, so it's worth repeating, that defining a ghost is like trying to nail mist to a brick wall with putty nails. When does a ghost become a poltergeist? What relationship does your average apparition have with a time-warp encounter – of whatever kind? And can a sound alone be enough to claim a ghostly rendezvous? Probably there are finickety differences but, for my book, if it makes the hair on the back of your neck curl, it's a supernatural experience (even if it is a bedroom encounter of the third kind and it has only just happened.) Thomas Main from Spennymoor in County Durham, who was a nursing student, now firmly believes there is another plane of existence. This is his story:

I have a very simple little tale to tell which may be of no interest to you at all but I shall give you the details and you can judge the facts for yourself.

It is something that happened to me and a bunch of my friends in 1991. I was almost 18 at the time and training to be a nurse. We trained under the old-fashioned system of nurse training in which 80% of the training was actually hands-on hospital work and only about 20% of the course was conducted in the classroom.

For the first six weeks of our course we were based at the training college in Hexham Hospital. There were three different sites of accommodation for student nurses and a bunch of us had drawn the short straw and were staying in the War Memorial Hospital. Basically this was an old geriatric hospital, still in use at the time, the top floor of which housed the accommodation. There were about 14 rooms in all, not all of which were occupied.

The place was very old and pretty grotty. I am sure you can imagine that as a bunch of idealistic teenagers away from home for the first time, we were not impressed. As is always the case in these places, it did not take long for the older students in the hospital to start telling us about the ghost.

Apparently the ghost was a young woman, possibly a trainee from years before, and she was said to haunt the hospital and student quarters. She had been seen and heard by loads of people over the years.

We all took the story with a pinch of salt. I did not believe in ghosts, although there were a lot of strange noises to be heard at night, footsteps in the corridor etc., but nothing that could not be written off in the morning as the sounds of an old building settling down for the night. We managed to get through five weeks of our stay with nothing more frightening happening than an occasional shortage of beer.

Although this sounds like a bad horror film, our last week was different.

Early in the week one of the girls, called Sarah, claimed that a figure had appeared and sat on her bed during the night. She was too terrified to move or call

out. The next day when she told the rest of us we all laughed and wrote it off as a bad dream or just an overactive imagination.

On the Thursday night a whole group of us went out to a local nightclub to celebrate the end of our six-week induction. We got back to the hospital around 2.30. Although we were all merry none of us was really drunk and there had been no drugs taken by anyone. We all had our last day of school on the Friday so no-one wanted to get into too bad a state. Five of us had brought home a takeaway and we went into the common room to enjoy our supper.

We began to talk about the ghost and Sarah's experience earlier in the week. A couple of the other girls had heard stories about the origins of the ghost and we all laughed at the contradicting tales and wrote the whole thing off.

Then the ghost laughed at us.

That may sound stupid but that is what happened. A loud "unearthly" laughter mocked us from the open doorway. It sounded neither male nor female, just really loud and derisive. It was as if it were taunting us. We all heard it. There was no one outside the room playing a trick, nor could there have been. No person could get into that position without us seeing them come and go.

It raises the hairs on the back of my neck just to remember it now. The tone of the laughter had no humour or playfulness to it, it was just frightening.

At first we all froze and then just stared at each other in disbelief. Then we all started to panic. Staying together in a tight group of five we went into one another's room to collect our toothbrushes and then we made a swift exit.

What a sight five terrified students must have made as they ran screaming from the building and across the fields to the neighbouring accommodation block. All five of us spent the rest of the night on an obliging friend's floor.

Although I have not had another direct experience of the supernatural I have believed undoubtedly in ghosts since that night. Although I have now given up nursing as a profession, during my time there were several occasions when I was aware of "something" leaving at the moment of a patient's death. You can just feel the presence or spirit or whatever you want to call it leave the physical body. It is a very tangible feeling.

28
Working holiday

Her skin was white as leprosy.

Samuel Taylor Coleridge *The Ancient Mariner*

SOMETIMES A HARMLESS night out can turn into anything but. Joe Daniels of Castle Bromwich was a student at the London School of Economics in 1950. He had been able to put off conscription into the armed forces to finish his degree course but he was finding it hard to survive. London wasn't the most hospitable city at that time. Most of the housing within reach of the university was either damaged or shared by noisy sets of students. And money was scarce. The government had launched a scheme a few years earlier that they imaginatively called "Holidays with Pay". What this did was provide students, and anyone else interested, with a chance to go out of the city and work (this was the holiday part) at picking fruit or harvesting crops. For this the jolly farmer allowed you to eat all the produce you wanted and paid you about a fifth of what the normal farm labourer was paid at this time. And farm labourers were notoriously underpaid.

Anyway, it was a change of environment and a chance to get away from six sharing a cold-water basement flat and the smell of unwashed socks, so Joe took it. He took the train to March in Cambridgeshire, was loaded onto the open back of a cattle truck and driven through the pouring rain to Outwell, about 30 miles away. One good thing came out of getting soaked to the skin by the time they passed through Outwell and turned into the grounds of what was left of Beaupre Hall he had struck up an acquaintance with another student hoping to turn the summer vacation into an opportunity to earn money to see her through the long winter – Pamela. The camp was situated in a sea of mud. Half a dozen or so salvaged army huts fitted out luxuriously with a pot-belly, coke-guzzling stove, wooden bunk-beds and Welsh miners perpetually looking, and often finding, a fight. Early next morning the rain had dwindled to a soul-dampening drizzle and the campers – that was what they were called, probably to make them feel some affinity with Butlin's Holiday Camp which was all the rage at the time – were loaded back onto the cattle trucks. Joe made sure he was next to Pamela and fended off anyone else who tried to strike up a relationship. At the farm they were handed a sack, to wear over their heads when the rain got heavier, and a couple of baskets. The intricacies of the picking explained to them, they were let out into a strawberry field watched over by somebody they assumed was the farmer but later turned out to be one of the labourers they were replacing.

This was to be the routine for the next month and Joe, after the first day, was wishing that he hadn't come. But things improved. His original motive had been financial. With the young and curvaceous Pamela on the scene his priorities changed. Pamela also liked the idea of skiving off for a bit of slap and tickle whenever the opportunity arose. Which wasn't very often. At the farm they were watched over by the farmer's employees, only too happy to point the finger at the slightest misdemeanour, and after work they were either so knackered they couldn't get up enough energy for a good session or couldn't find anywhere that offered some semblance of privacy. At the back of the camp, and strictly out of bounds, was the crumbling ruin of Beaupre Hall. In desperation the two lovers scaled the wall and barbed wire, fought their way through the undergrowth and found themselves at the bottom of a flight of broken steps. Cautiously they made their way inside. The ground floor was a treacherous mess of fallen masonry and garbage. The second floor was worse. There wasn't a floor. Finally they made it to the roof. This was solid and boasted a few dry corners so this became their regular trysting place.

By now the Joe-Pamela item was well known around the camp and the subject of a lot of ribald humour. They bore it well and didn't let it get them down. Besides, they had their special place to disappear to if they got fed up. For some reason the Welsh miners in Joe's hut had taken exception to him. Their attacks had always been verbal until one fine night when he was preparing to meet Pamela on the roof of the ruined Hall. The miners moved in, flicking Joe with the ends of their towels. At first he tried to laugh it off but as more got into the act he got angry and tried to fight back. It was hopeless. There were too many of them and years of shifting tons of coal a day had given them muscles of steel. It was humiliating and when Joe finally got away he was close to tears but seething with anger. Pamela was waiting for him on the roof. It took a long time for her to calm him down. She spread out the blanket she had brought and they made love. It wasn't too successful. Joe was too angry. They lay on the blanket each deep in thought. Joe was just about to try and make up for his earlier failure when he caught a movement out of the corner of his eye. For a

moment he feared that the miners had followed him and were going to make him look even more foolish than he already felt. He turned but there was nothing there. He decided the evening was ruined and they might as well leave their private place and go into Outwell and join the other campers at the pub. As he picked up the blanket he heard Pamela gasp. He dropped the blanket and spun round expecting the worst. Pamela was staring at something further along the walkway which ran behind the battlements. Joe felt more frightened than he had when the Welsh miners attacked him. Standing, shimmering in the moonlight, was the indistinct figure of a woman. She appeared to be dressed in a long, flowing white robe. She walked slowly towards them and Joe felt an aura of sadness push out towards him. He snatched a glance at Pamela. She was obviously seeing the same thing as he was. He wanted to run but the figure was between him and the steps leading down to the ground floor. Pamela began to cry. Later she claimed that it wasn't through fear or anything like that, she just felt uncontrollably sad. Without warning, the spectre vanished. Joe and Pamela stood there for a full five minutes before they could summon up the courage to run for the steps.

They never went back to the roof again and shortly after went back to their different colleges. Before they went they did try to casually elicit some information on the ghost but without asking a direct question they couldn't get the answers they wanted. They never met again. Joe Daniels got a second-class honours degree in Economics and went back to Manchester to become a successful banker. In the early seventies he was in Kings Lynn and decided to stop over and revisit the sight of his ghostly encounter. Older and more sure of himself, he pulled into the pub in Outwell and quizzed the barman about the Hall. As always happens the barman wasn't local and didn't know anything. Fortunately there was a

local at the bar and for the price of a pint and a lot of prompting Joe increased his knowledge of Beaupre Hall by about 2%. The old boy claimed, after Joe had prompted him to tell about the White Lady, that she was the daughter of the house whose father had sent her lover off to the war where he had soon been killed. Precisely which war seems to be irrelevant. The Great War or the Boer War. It might have been the Peninsular War – if he had known the dates. More likely it was the war against Spain or it might even have been 1066 and all that. Outwell is mentioned in the Doomsday Book so you can shut your eyes and take your pick. Discouraged Joe went and had a quick look at the Hall and tried to picture Pamela's face but all he felt was old.

29
Hobby

When by thy scorne, O murdresse, I am dead

John Donne *The Apparition*

BISHAM ABBEY, in anyone's books, has its fair share of sad apparitions. For one there's a ghostly figure of the young, beautiful daughter of the Earl of Salisbury. In the reign of King Stephen of goodness fame, Lady Montacute was the Abbess of Bisham Abbey. When her father came to say goodbye before going off to teach the Saracens a lesson he brought with him a good-looking and exceedingly randy squire. Turned on by her wimple he came on strong to her and soon had her out of the habit. The arrangement was that she should wait until everyone in the Abbey was asleep and then slip down to the river where her lover would be waiting with a boat. The first part of the operation went well. Safely installed in the boat the squire set off downstream. He had been thinking a lot about his ecclesiastical lover and he wanted to seal their union as soon as possible, so he pulled over to the bank and, in the parlance of the day, gave her one. This was not the brightest of ideas and gave credence to the old saying that if you want to get away with a bit of extra-marital listen to what is under your hat rather than your cod piece. Daddy's soldiers grabbed them as they were about to re-embark and dragged them back to the Abbey.

The esquire was on job training from a noble family so the zealous Earl couldn't just give him a good kicking and hang him by the neck so he locked him in the tower of the Abbey while he sorted out his daughter. Following the guidance of a good psychiatrist he beat hell out of her, then locked her in a cell without light or heat until she came to her senses. Meanwhile her lover in the tower, having tasted the forbidden fruits and finding them exceedingly moreish, decided on a tactic that at least claimed him a little attention. Trying to negotiate an aeriel passage from his prison to her cell he fell and did his back in. Lady Montacute decided that her ham-fisted lover had done enough to blight her prospects of being Abbess of the year and vowed to give him up. When the esquire recovered and found out what she had sworn he decided to take monastic vows as well. He probably thought that by doing so he could get back into the Abbey legitimately and then play it by ear. It might have been a good scheme if he hadn't had the organisational ability of Mr Bean. Discovered at it again, even the intervention of her powerful parent the Earl of Salisbury was not enough to stop the Abbess being walled up and her bungling lover starved to death. He had obviously had enough of the whole business and wasn't prepared to spend the rest of eternity in close spectral association with his lover. So, lonely and forlorn, she roams the river bank reliving the lustful moments when her squire had pulled over in the boat and gave her the twelfth-century equivalent of a back-seat bonk.

Another good haunting that seems attached to Bisham Abbey is that of Lady Hobby. She comes from the sixteenth century and is accused of infanticide. It seems that her father wanted a boy but was quite willing to acknowledge a girl as long as she acted like a boy. This didn't mean he wanted her to strut around in pantaloons and hose and make coarse jokes. He just wanted her to learn to read and juggle the figures of the estate so that his liege lord, Queen Elizabeth, wouldn't be tempted into cutting back his affluence. The novelty of a woman who could read and chat intelligently being only slightly below the enjoyment of watching a candle burning on a draughty night, she soon had a string of suitors also aware of Good Queen Bess's jealous eye on their property and looking for a creative accountant. The English ambassador seemed to be a good catch so Lady Hobby became Lady Bisham and went to France where her husband quickly succumbed to the water and died. Not before he had serviced her belly and begat her a son. However Lady Hobby was not the motherly type. She had no patience with a four-year-old who couldn't do simple algebra or recite Virgil. His lack of scholarly talent frequently drove her around the bend and she could only get relief from her frustrations by beating her inept son. The more she beat him the worse he became. Then tragedy struck. Lady Hobby belted him around the ear once too often and he died. It would have been too inconvenient to have to explain what had happened, so her ladyship got rid of the body and silenced anyone impertinent enough to ask awkward questions with an imperious stare. Rid of the maternal encumbrance Lady Hobby soon found another suitor, married and had several children. Either she had become more tolerant or her second brood were more adroit at dodging because there were no rumours of either disappeared or battered children laid at her door.

There is a saying that spite preserves and this certainly seems to have been the case with Lady Hobby. She lived to a crumbly old age and then popped off peacefully in her bed. Her ultimate peacefulness in life was not reflected in death. Hardly had the vault door clunked into place than reports from terrified servants and visitors started coming in. She was often seen gliding across the landings and entering certain rooms, probably the one her first born had slept in. Sometimes she was seen just standing in the corner of a room. She appeared to be washing her big white hands in an invisible basin as if trying to rid herself of bloodstains. The sightings went on for centuries so the description of the ghost is very detailed. One aspect that is interesting is that she is reported as having a black face. That it is the same ghost is corroborated by the constant action of hand washing as she tries to get rid of the damning bloodspots. Could this unquiet spirit be the source of inspiration for Bill Shakespeare when he was penning Macbeth? Or how about Othello?

It does seem as if someone has diligently removed all reference to the Hobby-Bisham issue. No record of a son exists. That either means that the whole story is a load of codswallop or the learned Lady Hobby was equally at home with an eraser as a quill. Workmen renovating part of the Abbey did cause a frisson of excitement when they uncovered a pile of Elizabethan children's books in a secret room. The room led off Lady Hobby's bedroom and had remained a secret for so long because it was hidden between two chimneys that were bent around the small chamber. Unfortunately there was no pathetic skeleton of a murdered child found in the room to bring the tale to a tidy end. Perhaps the bones are lying at the bottom of the Thames, which is only a few yards from Lady Hobby's room. That might explain why courting couples have often had their coitus interrupted by a black-faced phantom wandering along the river bank, wringing her hands in anguish.

30
The Ghostly Stool Pigeon

And where the offence is, let the great axe fall

William Shakespeare *Hamlet*

SOMETIMES THE TALES of ghostly hauntings are so far-fetched that they seem totally impossible to believe. In a way that is the difference between a good ghost story and one that is so over the top it just raises an eyebrow or a cynical laugh. But what if some venerable and respected figure is wheeled in to testify that the hard to believe story of spectral visitation is true. Someone like the Bishop of York or the Curate of Cripplegate. Here's an attested tale that is not the easiest to swallow but is all true – they say!

The city watchman, an "Old Charlie", was coughing his way along a dark alley in Cripplegate in London when he heard the sounds of someone being battered to death close by. Old Charlie gripped his cudgel more firmly and raised his oil lamp to let anyone who might be interested know he was about without him having to put his aching body in danger by getting too close. He called out a quavering "Who's there?" and was gratified to hear the sound of footsteps beating a retreat in the opposite direction. It wasn't hard to find the victim of the ruckus. He was slumped against the wall of the alley, his throat slashed to the backbone and gouting thick, warm blood into a gathering pool beneath him. His face had been battered so brutally that half his cranium had been removed and bone and brain tissue mixed with the blood around him. The alley was floored with compacted dirt that had turned to mud after a recent rain shower, and

footsteps bore witness to a fierce struggle. Robbery had been the prime motive and was borne out by the fact that the man's pockets had been emptied.

The murdered man's name was Stockton, a prosperous victualler, who lived close to the spot on which he had been mugged. It was a brutal killing, but brutal killings were ten a penny at this time and there were no Peelers around to carry out some sort of formal investigation.

Enter Mrs Greenwood who lived nearby in Grub Street. She was lying in bed when she heard someone trying the bedroom door. Not being in the first flush of youth she instantly realised that this was not a passionate suitor coming to have his evil way with her. Which left only a burglar. Before she could call out the neighbourhood watch, a tall, shrouded figure slithered into the room and stood at the foot of her bed. It was so unexpected it silenced her. What she had here was a class A spook operating on all levels. It slithered up to her bed, bent low and whispered one word – "Stockton!"

The word was on everyone's lips after the recent horrendous, and unsolved, murder. Not a word to tranquillise her fluttering heart. Before she could suffer a cardiac arrest the spectre placed an ice-cold hand on her shoulder and coerced her from her bed. She felt compelled to follow it. It waited patiently by the door while she threw on some clothes then led her down the stairs and out into the cold, moonlit streets. She hurried behind, wondering at herself for being stupid enough to set out on an unknown journey at the dead of night in the wake of what was obviously a ghost. They finally reached the river. The ghost pointed to one of the houses on the quay and again came over all monosyllabic. "Maynard ..." it said and, before Mrs Greenwood could ask him to repeat it, he had vanished and she woke up.

She didn't get much sleep for the rest of the night. The dream had been so vivid that she almost believed that her journey across town had actually happened. Next morning she was chatting to a friend, Mary Buggs, and they got so carried away with the dream that they decided to follow the route she had taken in her sleep and see what happened. Neither of them knew the area that the ghost had led her to but as the two friends retraced the journey, Mrs Greenwood was excited to see that it confirmed her memory in every detail. And there was the house, exactly the way she had dreamed it! They couldn't let it rest there. Mrs Greenwood banged on the door and it was answered by an old hag who clearly had never thought of entering any popularity stakes. Questioned about the possibility of Maynard being a tenant she snarled that he was away and wasn't expected back – ever! That seemed to be that so the ladies retraced their steps across town.

That night the ghost or whatever, appeared again. This time his tactics were different. He summoned her from the shelter of her bed and signalled to her to look into the mirror that hung on the wall beside her bed. What she saw terrified her. Reflected was not the tousled hair and baggy eyes of her sleep-interrupted face but the image of a brutal-looking man with dark glittering eyes and a horrible leering mouth. What made him unforgettable was a livid blemish on the side of his face.

The image vanished and Mrs Greenwood was left with her other worldly visitor. In a hoarse whisper it told her that what she had witnessed was Maynard. He told her to go to the house of a wire-cutter in Grub Street and get him to take Maynard by coach to the prison at Newgate. She had never heard of any wire-cutter in Grub Street but by now she was totally sold on the idea that she had a supernatural guru supervising her life, so when she woke up she immediately made inquiries and found that there was a wire-cutter in Grub Street by the name of Smith. Smith claimed to be a friend of Maynard and it took all of Mrs Greenwood's considerable powers of persuasion and quite a bit of money to get him to confess that he knew Maynard to be connected with a gang that had robbed and killed Stockton. With a little more coercion he promised, for ten pounds, to finger Maynard. At a public house, near Hockley-in-the-Hole, there was a long running card game at which Maynard frequently lost large sums of money. He was to lose more than money that particular night. Smith gave him a Judas kiss, the waiting constables moved in and Maynard got a free hackney-carriage ride to Newgate. Mrs Greenwood was amazed when she saw him. He looked exactly like the reflection she had seen in her bedroom mirror. Maynard wasn't too pleased to see her either. She had evidently haunted his dreams.

Maynard, bang to rights and facing a lonely 8p.m. drop, tried to buy some clemency by naming his comrades in crime – Marsh, Beel and Mercer. The constables went looking for them but they had evidently heard that Maynard was imitating a canary and absconded to other parts.

Her duty done, Mrs Greenwood retired to bed for some self-satisfied sleep. No sooner had her eyes closed and her mouth dropped open than the shrouded figure was at her side urging her to new heights of detection. Once more she followed him through the streets, but this time they finished up in Old Street. Her guide explained that this was where Marsh was holed up. Routine now, Mrs Greenwood woke up, called in the cops,

accompanied them to Old Street and had the satisfaction of seeing another villain carted off to the nick.

That night Mrs Greenwood retired to bed expecting to be called. Her excitement was such that it was nearly dawn before she finally dropped off. Sure enough the shrouded figure again came to her. This time he led her to the Borough prison yard and pointed to a heavily barred window on the second floor. In spite of the distance between her and the window she could make out every detail of the bloated, evil face pressed against the window. This was Marsh, the villain who had actually slashed Stockton's throat. Once again she accompanied the constables when they went to arrest Marsh for murder. He was in prison on a charge of issuing counterfeit coin, a charge punishable by hanging at this time so he had little to lose. Mrs Greenwood didn't need another visitation. Marsh was also happy to cut a deal and told his jailers exactly where they would find Beel. It didn't do any of the four villains any good trying to outdo each other with confessions about the others' culpability. All deals were off once they stood in the dock. Their sentences were a matter of routine and they all danced on the hangman's gibbet outside Newgate prison. In the court at their arraignment was Mrs Greenwood. She had more than a passing interest in what happened to them. She just prayed that she was done with ghostly visitations. The thought of having the four evil murderers coming looking for her was not an inducement to sleep.

Who or what was the shrouded figure? Who knows? Most probably the shade of the murdered Stockton. Why did he decide that Mrs Greenwood, whom he didn't know in life, was game for a haunting? Again there seems to be no known reason.

If you don't believe this tale you are calling the Bishop of York and the Curate of Cripplegate liars. Can you and your mortal soul really afford to do that?

Can we see a reflection of Dickens' *A Christmas Carol* in this story of nightly visitations that lead the main character on a journey and show her secrets that she couldn't possibly have known awake? Like Marley's ghost the shrouded man could interact with the haunted, could even exert a physical presence. It didn't need a lot of effort to seed the basic story with a moral and come up with Ebenezer Scrooge and his Christmas from hell.

There is also a strong element of Chaucer's *The Nun's Tale* with the revenant returning to sort out problems left behind in life.

31
Ḣitcḣḣiker

He travels fastest who travels alone.

Rudyard Kipling

BACK IN THE days when hitchhiking was considered a suitable activity for the young adventurer, there were many stories told about phantom pick-ups. Most are told from the view point of the driver of the vehicle who picked up the travelling spectre! There's an angelic old lady who stands outside the gates of Rayley Hall and is prepared to give any kind-hearted passing driver a thrill. She's in a hurry to get to Dunsington Cross. She's not a great talker but seems amicable enough until she gets where she's going – then she disappears. Sometimes her method of attracting the attention of the driver of a vehicle could be described as slightly bizarre. She hangs around on the branches of a tree and when she is picked out by the headlights of a passing car does a swallowdive with a short piece of rope knotted around her neck. Local drivers now know better than to stop and do the Good Samaritan act. But there's still a game afoot – out of the area drivers are still good for a laugh.

Another lady, pretty and attractively dressed in an expensive white dress, added a certain something to a day out by the seaside for a family from Montpelier in France. Squashed into a tiny Renault in the hot afternoon they were not too pleased when the driver saw the white-clad girl walking along the side of the road and decided to give her a lift. The car already had a front-seat passenger and the two wives in the back. Getting the new woman into the car wasn't easy. The passenger in front had to get out so that the taciturn passenger could squeeze into the back between the two women. The driver set off and tried to explain his actions by telling the newcomer that it wasn't safe to be walking the road by herself. It would be dark in less than an hour. It was probably said as much for his wife's benefit as the hitchhiker. Still she didn't comment. They were approaching a bend in the road when the woman suddenly became very agitated. She sat bolt upright and pointing frantically ahead, screamed, presumably in French, "Look out for the turns, look out for the turns!!"

There was enough panic in her voice to make the driver stomp on the brakes and send the car into a bit of a slide. By the time he had gathered it up and brought it under control, the cause of the problem had vanished. One moment she was sitting jammed between the two ladies – the next they were alone. The two couples got out of the car and looked around. They didn't believe in vanishing hitchhikers and thought that in some mysterious fashion the woman might have jumped out without them seeing – in a two-door Renault 5? They found nothing so reported the incident to a sceptical police inspector and still dine out on the story.

A much more social ghost is Rose White. Not only does she not appear to know she's dead but she is still intent on having a good time. Joy Hendrix, her husband Bob and a friend called Jack were driving along the road to a beach north of LA when they saw Rose standing at the side of the road apparently looking for a lift. They didn't know it was

Rose, of course, but she looked so gorgeous in her billowing white dress and windswept blonde hair that they just had to stop. It was quite a chilly night but Rose asked if she could wind down the window as she felt hot. The others, in heavier clothes, didn't like to look like wimps so they told her to go ahead. Jack was quite clearly smitten with the beautiful girl and when they reached the club where they were going to dance he asked her if she would care to join them. She agreed. She was full of life and humour and Jack was congratulating himself on his luck. Then he asked her to dance. It was like dancing with an animated iceberg. Although the temperature in the club was well into the 90s she felt like she had just stepped out of a refrigerator. He mentioned it to Bob and he gave her a twirl just to make certain his friend wasn't trying to promote their new friend as some sort of ice princess. He had to agree. In spite of appearances she didn't appear to have a drop of warm blood in her veins. Jack eyed her up again and decided that he didn't care. She was too much of a catch to give up because she hadn't reached room temperature.

When Joy decided she had seen enough of the two men ogling the lightly clad and decidedly pneumatic girl she called quits and led them out to the car. Jack got to sit near the frigid blonde on the way home and managed to extract her address although she refused to let them take her home. She stood at the side of the road and waved goodbye until they went out of sight around the next corner. Jack couldn't sleep that night. All he could think about was the lovely girl with a temperature an Eskimo would have envied. Next day he cajoled Joy to take him to the address that Rose had given him. It turned out to be a nunnery. It was a bit of a stopper but Jack was all fired up now and wanted to meet the girl again, vows or no vows. When Jack explained his mission to the Mother Superior she was instantly interested. Without explaining anything she took out a photograph album and placed it in front of them and asked them to go through it and see if they could find Rose White. This they did fairly

easily. There weren't a lot of gorgeous blondes amongst the wimpled nuns. The Mother Superior, working the situation for maximum theatrical effect, said she would take them to Rose White at once. She led them to the cemetery just outside the nunnery gates. There, on a tombstone, was the name Rose White. The Mother Superior explained that Rose had died many years before, how many she didn't say – which makes her final statement a little hard to believe.

"Rose White has been seen three times before and it's always on the date of the day she was buried. She only comes back every 15 years."

So, up until then you were willing to be counted in the ranks of the believer. But those last words kill it stone dead. If Rose comes back every 15 years and assuming that her first visitation was 15 years after her death and she has been seen three times before, it means that she died 60 years before Joy, Bob and Jack partied with her. As this incident has a sell-by date of the early 1950s, Rose must have died around the turn of the nineteenth century. And yet she knew about cars, was quite happy to wind down a window, had no trouble with dancing to the kind of music that must have sounded strange to 60-year-old ears, and this is the capper, none of the party who allegedly picked her up thought there was anything strange about her dress. Or was she a modern ghost who kept up with twentieth-century fashions?

These are all ghosts that appeared out of the past, reacted briefly with the present and then disappeared. The story of Bernard Calloway who lives on the north-east coast near Rhyl had a very different tale to tell. He was serving in the Royal Air Force at the time and had been posted to Lytham St Anne's to do a driving course. He soon got to know the surrounding area pretty well. He also got to know Helen. Helen worked in the camp as a civilian clerk and had been in charge of the rotas for the learner drivers. When Bernard finally passed his driving test he asked if he could stay on at the camp. They were short of driving instructors so, in spite of his relatively short experience of driving, he was put on an

instructors' course. By this time Helen and Bernard were a well-knit item and there was talk of marriage. It was Bernard's usual practice to cycle to Helen's, just short of ten miles away, in the evening, have dinner and anything else that was on offer before cycling back to camp. One night, fully sated he cautiously mounted his bike, waved goodbye – and found he had a flat tyre. With no all-night pass there was nothing to do but walk. He had only gone about a mile when an old-fashioned lorry pulled up beside him. He gratefully climbed aboard. A young man sat impassively behind the wheel. Bernard explained that he had to get back to camp and the driver looked at him expressionlessly and slipped the clutch. Bernard tried to get a conversation going but the driver didn't respond so he fell silent. Really silent. There didn't seem to be any noise coming from anywhere. As the lorry was old and decidedly rickety this was spooky. Bernard was also aware that the temperature in the cabin seemed to be below freezing. Still, it was better than walking so he snuggled down in his RAF greatcoat and relived the energetic evening he had just had with his fiancée.

The lorry came up to a level-crossing. There seemed to be nobody about and the driver sat as if he had no intention of getting out and finding someone to open the gate. Then Bernard saw a notice that said that the crossing was unmanned between certain hours and this was one of them. Bernard mentioned the new intelligence to his driver and was again struck by the fact that he got no reaction. Pissed off he made a big display of opening the door and jumping to the ground. As he pushed the first gate back the lorry was still standing there. He turned to push the other gate out of the way and when he turned back the lorry had disappeared. It hadn't gone over the level-crossing and the narrow lane up to the crossing was hedged on both sides; it was a hundred yards before a turn in the road could have concealed it. And Bernard's back hadn't been turned long enough to allow the lorry to reverse that far without him hearing something. Or

maybe not!! Bernard walked back to the camp and didn't tell anyone about his unusual experience. He didn't want to be the butt of every joker and prankster in his unit. But he did tell Helen. Her reaction surprised him. The phantom lorry was well known in the area. The story goes that during the Great War the driver had been employed to carry explosives and ammunition from the camp to a firing and grenade range. On one of his runs something set off a grenade and the whole shebang went up, killing the driver. Since that time he has often been seen on the road at night. And it wasn't unknown for him to pick up a hiker bound for the camp where his troubles started.

One last ghostly hitchhiker concerns the ubiquitous black dog. A driver on the road between Woodbridge and Colchester nearly had an accident when he swerved to avoid a black dog that ran out in front of him. The car hit the earth bank at the side, but luckily straightened up and gave the driver a chance to apply the brakes before any serious damage was done. Cursing he got out to check his wheels and was surprised to see the dog sitting in the road looking at him. Thinking the dog might have been hurt he made all the usual nauseating noises people make when they try to convince an animal that they are friendly and the dog reciprocated nicely and walked slowly towards him. It seemed friendly but when the driver tried to pat him it moved adroitly out of arm's-length. Satisfied that the animal wasn't hurt the driver opened the car door to get in. Before he could move the dog streaked passed him and sat in the back seat. The man tried to entice him out but the dog refused to move. There was nothing for it but to bribe it into quitting the back seat with a piece of chocolate. No luck!

When he got home and looked in the back – no dog. He swears that there is no way the dog could have got out of the car without him knowing. But it had gone and he had a nice little story to tell the wife and take her mind off his beery breath and buckled coachwork.

32
Harry Price

And spectral dance, before the dawn,
A hundred Vicars down the lawn;
Curates, long dust, will come and go
On lissom, clerical, printless toe;
And oft between the boughs is seen
The sly shade of a Rural Dean.

Rupert Brooke

THERE WAS A TIME when Harry Price was practically a household name. There wasn't a ghost in Britain that didn't quake at the name. Especially those that confined their haunting to Borley Rectory in Essex. Ghosts had been knocking around the red-brick pile since it was built by the Reverend Henry Bull in 1863 but it wasn't until Harry Price came on the scene that they got their true recognition. Then there wasn't a creak or a whisper that wasn't recorded by the fearless ghostbuster. One of the most famous photographs, taken presumably after the rectory had been pulled down, is a brick *floating* in mid-air. The mind boggles. Then there was the nun who was often seen hurrying along one of the garden paths. These were the stories that gave Harry the opening he wanted to disclose his remarkable discoveries.

But let's start at the beginning.

The Bull family occupied the rectory for nearly three-quarters of a century. First Harry, the builder and patriarch who paid for it, then his son, Henry junior, who finally lost it when the living was taken from the Bull family and given to the Reverened G.E. Smith and his wife. There were rumours flying around already about paranormal activity, promoted mainly by the villagers who thought the menacing old pile just had to have a ghost. The Smiths rather liked the idea of living dangerously so put out a few stories of their own. Somehow it got to the ears of a reporter on the *Daily Mail* and he did what all good reporters with a soggy notepad and a well-licked pencil do – he wrote it up big. He soon dug up the interesting little fact that 12 clergymen had turned the living down before Smith had been coerced into accepting it. He put this down to the fact that Borley Rectory was a hot house of raging ghosts. It, seemingly, didn't occur to them that the Borley living, buried in the wilds of pre-Essex-girl Essex wasn't exactly a fought-over appointment. Harry Price felt the same way. He was already a well-known figure in the ghosthunting world. Borley Rectory was just what he wanted to make it through to the big time.

The *Daily Mail* winkled out parishioners who swore they had seen the ghost of a nun glide along one of the paths leading to the rectory and disappear through a wall. This nun ran to a timetable. She always made her presence known on July 28th. The story that accompanied the peripatetic nun was that she was a novice in the medieval convent that predated the rectory. She became romantically entangled with one of the lay monks from the monastery on the site later used by the rectory and planned to elope with him. They were to be aided by a friend, another lay monk. First part of the plan went to schedule. A coach and pair was parked by the gates of Bures convent with the horses warmed up and, at the appointed hour, the nun shinned down a rope into the arms of her waiting lover. Urged on by his brother monk, lover boy and his true love piled into the coach, whipped up the horses and set off for pastures new. They didn't get far. Medieval abbots didn't get where they were by letting libidinous monks make off with the local fiancées of Christ whenever they felt the urge. Jealous, and presumably frustrated, monks leaped aboard fast steeds and soon found the sexually united couple in a hostelry not too far up the road. They dragged them back to Borley Abbey as it then was, gave them a good scourging and passed sentence without any nonsense about a trial or anything that was likely to come between the benign Abbot and the guilty. The nun was bricked up in one of the less salubrious parts of the house of God and the monk was strangled by his forgiving brothers.

Another ghostly tableau vivant came from the time of Henry Bull's son Harry. He swore that he often witnessed a coach and horses gallop at a frantic pace away from the rectory. When the story got a little old-hat he spiced it up by claiming that the phantom coach was driven by two headless horsemen.

There was also another story that was touched on at the time but was not given the credence it deserved. It was said that shortly after the rectory was built a young girl was seen hanging out of a window on the second floor. Her screams alerted the household but before anyone could come to her aid she fell.

As a serious spook detective Harry Price couldn't pass up the chance of investigating such a notorious location and, before the newspapers had time to be wrapped around a piece of cod and six pennorth, he was standing on the doorstep demanding admittance. With him was his secretary who also had a lot of experience of staking out deserted rooms in haunted houses and could be expected to support Harry in his endeavours. Price picked up where the *Daily Mail* reporter had left off. The Smiths, now enjoying the fame that comes with toughing it out in a house teetering on the brink of hell, were soon telling Harry stuff they had forgotten to tell the reporter. They claimed that shortly after moving in the manifestations had begun to make themselves noticeable. First of all there were furtive whispers and moaning and a woman's voice begging, "Don't Carlo, don't!" Which is rather interesting because in that part of Essex there is one of the biggest conclaves of Italians in the country. There were also strange and mysterious footsteps and a light that appeared in the window of one of the bedrooms of an unused wing of the building. The strange goings on, reported by the rector were eagerly testified to by two maids who may or may not have had a vested interest in Carlo.

Harry Price accepted what they had to say as a basis for a good investigation, unloaded his equipment and moved in. Haunting couldn't have been better. Almost immediately things started to happen. Objects started whizzing about, propelled by unseen forces, voices screamed and whispered as was their wont, pottery mysteriously exploded and there was the sound of footsteps – always in another part of the house. The members of the Smith household pooh-poohed all this as nothing to what they had experienced over the years. Before he came they had been subjected to spontaneous combustion, wall writing, bell ringing, clandestine fumbling, smells, headless horsemen, singing – you name it, they'd had it. Initially direct experience by Price was a little mundane and limited to strange bells ringing and a little poltergeist activity. Harry decided that the seat of the manifestations was the Blue Room – the location for one of the earliest supernatural sightings of the girl hanging out of the window. Without a qualified medium to guide them through the tortuous path to the other side, the results were a little disappointing. However Harry Price did come into astral contact with Henry Bull, the son of the builder of the property. He also worked out a contact trick with the other world that cut out all the time wasting of a seance. In future there wasn't to be any fumbling around for a topic that would suit both ghost and ghosthunter. Harry could just turn up and ask for the duty spook.

Harry also made a breakthrough with the gardener. He was having real problems with the three Bull sisters who had passed over some years before. They were, in their ethereal form, incorrigible and wouldn't leave him alone. A month after Harry moved in, the Smiths moved out. In a statement they said that the poltergeist, or whatever was providing the entertainment, wasn't the reason they were leaving. Which only left Harry!

The house stood empty for a year with only the occasional report of anything untoward. Then the Reverend Lionel Foyster moved in. He was a cousin of the ecclesiastical Bulls and didn't believe in all the goings on that had been reported in the newspapers. Harry, sad to have lost a source of psychic income, kept in touch but it was a year before the Foysters decided they needed his professional services. The hauntings had started again. This time the malevolence was directed at one of the rector's daughters, Marianne. She wasn't a

well girl and got more than her fair share of knocks and harassment when the presence was being unreasonably violent. Harry himself was not immune from persecution and on the very night he arrived at Borley for the second time he was subjected to a spirited prank. Reverend Foyster recommended a rather nifty wine he had recently acquired and poured the ghostbuster a glass. You can imagine the consternation when Harry sipped it and it had turned into red ink – vintage unknown. It made him more than ready to accept what had become known as Marianne's messages. These were notes scrawled on convenient walls, addressed to Marianne and suggesting things that an 11-year-old shouldn't know about. Questioned expertly by Harry, Marianne admitted she hated the damp old rectory and would do anything to get away. Because of her attitude and the "messages", Harry suspected that the girl was the source of the paranormal activities. It had long been mooted by those in the know that pre-pubescent girls carried a lot of weight, astralwise, and had a special "in" with poltergeists on the look-out for a way to the fireside hearth. Marianne finally got her way and the family moved out in 1935. Harry played up the "most haunted house in England" card but, without a psychically battered and abused family, the story was beginning to flag. So Harry did the only thing a ghostbuster could do in the circumstances and took a lease on Borley Rectory.

Harry Price and a friend, Ellic Howe, moved in and got down to a scientific appraisal of just what they had leased. They spent a lot of time drawing chalk circles around movable objects and got some satisfaction from finding they had moved next time they looked. They also got some unidentified footsteps and plenty of tragic sighs. Carlo was not heard of again. It was what Harry wanted. When the Foysters had been there he had been under some obligation to see things through the limited range of his host's spectacles. Now that he had stuck his

hand in his pocket and leapt centre stage he wanted more than a few disturbed chalk circles and ambiguous noises off. He came up with a scheme that would help out with the expenses and also give him the kudos of running a show with a high-kicking chorus line. He advertised in the newspaper for psychic assistants. Qualifications: do what you're told and listen to Uncle Harry. Out of a couple of mailbags of replies he selected 20 who were able to pay the "expenses" and had an interest in bolstering up Borley's flagging reputation. Drawing on his long and intimate relations with ghosts and poltergeists, he drew up the Harry Price book of dos and don'ts for the amateur ghostbuster. Things looked up when a skeleton of a woman was found bricked up in the cellar. Harry would have liked to prove it was the mortal remains of the hot-blooded nun but there was an inconvenient gap of 55 years or so. He decided that was a bit tenuous so low-keyed it as a possible secondary cause of the manifestation. Assiduously Harry had his apprentices going around the house marking objects that could possibly move and then making copious notes when they didn't. Some of his helpers got fed up when nothing spine-tingling happened and left. To be fair, Harry did his best to juice up the unspectacular proceedings. Someone saw a shadow and he unconditionally named it as the shade of the famous nun. But he was clutching at straws. A seance seemed to provide an answer. The family Glanville claimed occult powers and got a hot line to the garrulous spirit of Harry Bull. Reverend Bull junior went with the story of the randy monk and his flighty nun. It was a little inconvenient that extant records showed that there had never been an Abbey on the site, not even before King Henry had made an antique art form out of knocking them about a bit. The obliging Harry Bull was contradicted by another know-all on the astral plane who said forget the long-running medieval monk and nun

story and come forward a few hundred years. We still get a nun but a nun with a name. Marie Laure was French and ruined by an English holy man who should have known better. When she turned up at the Abbey, her English high-flyer got rid of the problem and buried the body in what was later to become a cellar of Borley Rectory. Ah well, that's all right then. It explains the skeleton found there by Harry and his band.

The inconvenience of the Borley Rectory story, as told by Harry Price, is that the monastery that preceded it never existed. It is probably to overcome this problem in logistics that in later years the action, the putative action, was directed across the road to the church. A church had been known to exist on the site for the required number of centuries. Until the rectory, now known as Borley Priory, burned down in 1939, the stories about inexplicable happenings at the priory came out of Essex. Not a few with Harry Price's thumbprints on them. Then Harry died! It was the signal for all those great haunting supporters who had used him as their shining light for decades, to begin to doubt. They accused Harry of being a fraud and a showman. Even the dear old *Daily Mail*, which had launched Harry on his Borley career, accused him of faking to get the results he wanted. The Reverend Smith was trotted out and held up his hands, wide eyed, and remembered that the hauntings hadn't really started until Harry arrived. And the famous wine into ink incident? Smith sadly had to confess that it probably had more to do with legerdemain than psychic phenomena.

Then S.H. Glanville, one of Harry's loyal assistants and the author of more than a few seances during that time, criticised him for his lack of professionalism and not keeping a proper diary. On the other hand Glanville claimed to be a very model of clinical expertise. Although trashing everything that had involved Harry he claimed that his seances and his dialogue with Henry

Bull and other astral visitors were as pukka as a sworn statement on the gallows.

Over the years various ghostbusters have tried to work up a little interest in the site but, beyond the occasional floating brick and flickering, nunlike shadows, most of the action now seems to be centred on the church. And that's not enough to get most testifiers' juices flowing.

Perhaps the next ghost up will be that of Harry Price. The Borley Rectory made and destroyed his reputation – enough to make any ego come back a-haunting.

The goings-on at Borley Rectory are a bit reminiscent of the Peter O'Toole film *High Spirits*. That has a randy lover chasing his fleeing bride on a cyclical path until it is diverted by the arrival of a hot-blooded American. It's got the other type of ghostly hauntings, too. Rapping on doors, shrieks, falling bodies, faces at the window – and that's only the servants. The snapper in *High Spirits* is that all the make-believe wasn't necessary. There were ghosts there a-plenty anyway.

33
Sparky Old Girl

GRIZEL IS AN old girl who would get my vote every time. Even on the gallows she was in there hissing and spitting and not letting the bastards drag her down. She wouldn't have been on the gallows if it wasn't for her brother going soft in the head and telling everyone he was in league with the devil.

Major Tom Weir was considered one of the stalwarts of society in Edinburgh. He had a distinguished career and had done his part in the struggles in Ireland to keep the Roman Catholics in their place. When he retired he went to live in one of the more salubrious areas close to Parliament Square. Grizel, his spinster sister, moved in as his housekeeper and for a quarter of a century he lived a refined and proper life. As the Major aged he became more aggressive and erratic. This was covered up by his devoted sister and few acquaintances knew what a pain he had become. Then, when he was in his seventies, he started to talk about the devil. At first his sister took no notice: she had become used to his rantings and took his new avenue of thought as nothing more than the harmless prattling of an old man whose sand was running out. It took a serious turn when he turned up at a Proctor's house and wanted to confess that he had been a one-man crime wave for years. When the Proctor was obviously not going to buy his story he switched ground. What about witchcraft? This was a bit more like it, but the lawyer had known Weir for years and didn't fancy hauling him in on a witchcraft charge. He advised the old warrior to go home and lie down in a darkened room.

Unfortunately the Major had now found a hobbyhorse he could ride to death and went at it at a gallop. He told the tale to everybody whom he could make listen – a tale of seances and pacts, ritual slaughter and spell-casting. At last he got somebody to listen. But all it got him was a visit from a doctor. The doctor passed him as A1 and advised him to take more water with it. Major Weir ignored his doctor's advice and made such a nuisance of himself that in the end, badgered by the ecclesiastical authorities who could see some mileage in a witchcraft trial, the Proctor had to order his arrest. This should have been a salutary lesson to the old windbag but, now that he had the attention he craved, his imagination went wild. Without any prompting he was telling tales of exhilarating rides through the night on the backs of demons, orgies in the cellar of his house and the sacrifice of children and virgins to the Lord of the Underworld. When he had finished cataloguing his own misdemeanours he started on his sister. She became everything from a broomstick-commuting witch to a blood-imbibing succubus. Before Grizel knew what was happening she was standing in the dock beside him accused of the capital crime of witchcraft. He revelled in it. Grizel could see the writing on the wall. As eagerly as they had tried to shut Weir up, the prosecutors now prompted him to confess. So good was he in the dock that in the spring of 1790 he was sentenced to death. So was his sister. She had been found guilty by association and on the word of her patently deranged brother. They both died. He by strangulation and she by hanging. He went to meet his Maker quietly enough, satisfied in a job well done. His ballsy sister wasn't so compliant. When they led her to the gallows she ripped off her clothes and

screamed that if she was going to be dishonoured she might as well go all the way. It was a plucky ploy but it didn't deter the hangman who had seen it all before.

The reputation the Weir siblings had won at their trial was enough to taint the house on West Bow where they had lived, and, if the court was right, pursued their devilish persuasions. It became a millstone round the estate agent's neck and was unsaleable for years after the execution. Legends built up about evil doings behind the shutters. Spectral coaches driven by headless horsemen were reported arriving at the door and hideous creatures with dark, amorphous shapes, skull heads and fiery eyes were seen to alight from them and join the party going on inside. And there always seemed to be a party going on inside. The sound of music and dancing accompanied by horrible shrieking and laughter so sadistic it turned milk sour in the teat, was often to be heard. Sometimes, late at night, the sound of Grizel's spinning wheel could be heard as she spun spells way into the night. She was also seen looking out of the windows as if she were waiting for someone to return. Probably she was waiting for the Major so that she could pursue him through the

hereafter for the dirty trick he had played on her. Major Tom was often seen coming out of the house and riding off on one of the headless horses. Observers swore that as the horse passed, flames flared up from its hooves.

There's always someone up for a bargain and, after years of lying derelict, an offer of any sort was welcome. When a Spanish couple named Patullo offered to take over the lease the lawyers acting for the now defunct Weir family snatched their hands off. It didn't take the Patullos long to decide that however low the rent was the West Bow house wasn't for them. The first night they were there they were woken by a spectre calf that walked through the closed door and jumped onto their bed. It sat there looking at them for a while, then slowly disintegrated. That was enough for the Patullos. They didn't want any truck with ghostly goings-on. Before the dew had dried in the morning sun they had packed their belongings and were up the road. That sealed the fate of the building and in 1830 it was razed to the ground. The story became quite celebrated and even Sir Walter Scott couldn't avoid penning a word or two about the hauntings and Grizel's humming spinning-wheel.

34
Black Death

They hear the tolling bell
Reaching across the landscape of hysteria, to where
Religion stands, the church blocking the sun.

Stephen Spender

THE TOUR INDUSTRY for unusual walks has grown fantastically during the last decade. Probably it has always been there. Who could miss the chance to show tourists over the haunts of some of our favourite bad boys: Jack the Ripper, Harry the Hat, the Richardsons etc. But ghosts, ghouls and vampires? They have always done their own PR in the past by scaring some poor bloke witless and leaving him to testify to their effectiveness. Now there seems to be a tour guide on every street in the cities of Great Britain, each with a story to tell and each with an angle. Some of the stories tend to be pretty inaccurate – but who am I to talk. Edinburgh, in many ways, is a fairy-tale city. A grim fairy-tale city, if you'll excuse the pun. It's been cleaned up no end in the last 20 years or so and no longer deserves its old soubriquet of "Old Reekie". Unless "Old Reekie" means something more than it appears to. One or two tourist guides haunt the streets and have a number of ghosts on tap but the one that taps into the vein is a story of dire happenings in Mary King's Close around 350 years ago – the time of the Black Death. Who Mary King was isn't important. She predates our saga.

Alexander King was a powerful lawyer. A Roman Catholic. Not a particularly popular religion at the time.

Fervent about his faith and having a few bob in his pocket he was happy to help other Catholics in the area. Then, as now, it wasn't what you know but whose pocket you could get your hand in that mattered. Before long there was a whole colony of Catholics living around Alexander King's Close, as it was then known, and dragging the neighbourhood down. The Black Death was believed to be carried on the soles of their feet, like foot and mouth disease without the mouth. And Alexander King's army of supporters tended to be drawn from the poorer classes. These were lucky if they could find an old sack to use as a kilt so the chance of them possessing a pair of shoes was non-existent. Result – the Black Death was marched into the Close and spread like an overflowing sewer. It was the sort of opportunity the city fathers were looking for. Setting a precedent for Warsaw, they herded all the Catholics into the area around King's house, then built a high brick wall around it. For justification – should anyone ask – they trotted out the old arguments that were always cliches in witch trials, the infected were carriers who were actually causing the plague. Unexplained was why the alleged perpetrators seemed to be the only victims. Probably the citizens of Edinburgh were unaware of just how many of the King's Close victims had the disease and thought they were being incarcerated because they were healthy and causing the sickness in the non-Catholic community. Whatever – about 1,000 men, women and children were bricked up and left to die. Among them were about 100 who had no plague symptoms and were perfectly healthy. Summer came and added to the problem. No arrangements had been made by the city authorities to get rid of the plague victims. The growing mountain of bodies stored in the open with no possibility of burial in the small area, began to add to the problem. The stink was unbelievable – and the rats!! It was the smell that finally brought some sort of relief. Unlike the diseased and dying inmates of the ghetto, the odour was able to escape the brick walls and spoil the comfort of the Protestants in the vicinity. Their protests finally got the civic authorities in gear and they appointed a pest control officer to figure out a way to clear the bodies without spreading the disease. By now there was a huge pile made up of over 500 dead. The pest controller appointed a couple of men from the ghetto to sort out the problem. It was a long, hard summer. As soon as the mountain of bodies looked like it was diminishing, there would be a fresh supply. And the men removing the bodies weren't immune to the disease. By now there were very few healthy bodies in the enclave and those who were didn't fancy risking contamination by getting involved in the burial. Things got so bad, and space so limited, that the survivors were reduced to hacking the bodies to pieces and disposing the parts wherever it was convenient. This presented a problem to the dispossessed spirits. The usual ghost tends to inhabit, or non-inhabit, a place where something tragic or dramatic happened. This described the Alexander King's Close about as accurately, if a little unemotionally, as you could get it. But then there was the complication of all those hacked-off limbs distributed piecemeal about the city. A large

number of hauntings seem to be concerned with the restless spirit looking for something. Heads come high up in the order of body parts. King Charles is a well-known case. Maybe it was something in the air at that time? His case was relatively simple. All he had to search for was his head. Pity the poor plague victim in Edinburgh. His limbs struck asunder he must have been driven schizophrenic looking for the bits and pieces. Time hasn't reunited the component parts of a well-matured ghost and Alexander King's Close is haunted by unidentified parts of victims of the plague. Even Alexander King seems to have been deconstructed. The Close was renamed Mary King. Why? That is obviously another story. A story that has drawn those looking for a spectral thrill from all over the world.

Quite recently a Japanese lady, a perennial tourist, decided to check out the Scottish afterlife and visited Mary King's Close. In one of the rooms, which she names "the little girl's room" but wasn't using the euphemism for lavatory purposes, she inexplicably felt terribly sad and wanted to cry. Then she became aware of a little girl. She quickly identified its form as not of this world and opened communications with her. Luckily the Japanese lady was able to converse in whatever is the celestial language and extracted the girl's story. It seems the little girl, let's call her Mary to forge a link with the Close, was bricked up with all the other Catholics when Edinburgh felt the need to cauterise its unhealthy parts. She fortunately – or unfortunately, depending how you look at it – had not contracted the plague virus at this time. Her mother, with the indomitable power that is vouchsafe to mothers when their offspring are at risk, managed to get her out of the carnal house. Once outside and heading for safety the little girl discovered that in the hysteria of being separated from her mother she had left her favourite doll behind. Before anyone could stop her she got back inside. The authorities left her there. She had been given a chance, they had shown their humane face and she had spurned them. What had happened to the doll? Nobody knew or cared. Her mother, dying by the moment, tried to get the girl, *sans* doll, once more over the wall to freedom. She was too weak and the girl fell, badly hurting her leg. It made it impossible for her to run away and inevitably she caught the plague and died. This produced a disquiet spirit that, until the advent of the Japanese lady, roamed the Close looking for her doll. She is at rest now. The Japanese lady ordered that a doll, similar to the one described by the ghost of the little girl, should be placed in the room. This was done and since that day nothing has been seen or heard from the little plague victim.

It couldn't have all been down to despondency in the Close during the plague. A couple of nurses who decided to spend the night there to aid a charity got through the night undisturbed but complained the next morning about the noise coming from the party upstairs. This simple statement raises an eyebrow: the only people in the Close that night were the nurses. No boisterous drunks or raving teenagers. What they discovered was that a tavern had stood on the site, post-plague, and it seems that what the nurses heard was a spiritual revival in the lay sense.

The real spooky one, claimed by the official guide to be a first haunt experience, concerns a party of tourists he was doing his best to frighten to death by the recital of tales spectral and macabre. He had worked up his act so well that it wasn't unusual for susceptible amateur ghosthunters to come over all unnecessary and faint. Experience had taught him to watch for the signs and do whatever was required. One day he was waxing particularly spectral when he saw a woman on the edge of the group showing all the signs of a diver. Before he could get to her she turned white and pitched forward in a dead faint causing serious damage to her nose and mouth. Scaring the punters is what he is paid for but bringing them back damaged is not on the programme. The guide tried to comfort her but, when she recovered, she looked at him with haunted eyes, wrenched herself away and cowered in the corner. It brought an early close to the tour and the lady was carted off to the hospital. When she had quietened down the guide went to see her to apologize. She wouldn't have any of that. Her reaction at the time might have been a little OTT but now she had time to consider she realised that she had a story that was going to take care of her dining arrangements for years to come. She tried the story out on the guide.

When he was giving his spiel she was standing towards the back of the group but she had become aware of a dark presence separating itself from the shadows and standing behind him. Not sure of the evidence of her own eyes she moved around to the side for a better view. What she saw made her follicles flinch. The shadow had the form of a woman dressed all in black. She walked several times around the guide as if trying to work out what he was doing there and who he was. Without warning, the black shadow walked straight through the guide and headed towards the bug-eyed tourist. Before she could move, the dark entity walked straight through her and into the wall behind.

Neither the guide nor tourist had felt anything when their bodies were invaded but the experience was enough to screw up the lady's mind. It seems that the tourist lady wasn't the only one to "see" what she saw. Some of the others in the party had also seen something and congratulated the guide on the "acting" and asked him how it was done.

This story was sent in by Bill Lindsay of Lochgelly and confirmed by Mercat Tours of Edinburgh. There you go.

35
Drummers

THERE IS A very strong connection between ghosts and timpani. Most seances are held with the understanding that the chance for a cosy fireside chat is going to be slightly laborious as the other party involved is probably only going to communicate by table rapping. And then only to give the obligatory one tap for "yes" or two for "no". Or vice-versa – depending on the sophistication and versatility of the medium. It comes as no surprise, therefore, to find that there is a plethora of drummers from all parts of the globe, who have selected or been forced to spend their eternity bashing away at a pigskin. One of the most prominent of these is the Tedworth Drummer. Strictly speaking it's not a ghost's ghost. No mistaking the phenomenon for a friend dressed up in a white shirt with a repertoire limited to a couple of "whoo-whoos" and some doglike panting. And the supposed agent for all the special effects that were heard and seen was not necessarily dead.

Cause and effect are a little tenuous. What happened? The manifestation, as we in the ghostbusting business like to call it, was centred on the house at Tedworth owned by magistrate John Mompasson. He was married and had produced several assorted offspring and was distinguished by being an overbearing busybody. He was away making another poor miscreants life hell when the drummer moved in. Aided, it must be said, by the magistrate himself. At a trial a few days before he had confiscated a drum from a man doing a bit of busking in the High Street. His problem was, and this was around the middle of the seventeenth century, that he hadn't a permit. The more things changed the more they stay the same, it seems. Anyway, the instrumentalist was understandably miffed at the loss of his means of support and was banged up in jail, pushing out bushels of hatred at the man who had put him there. This is only mentioned in passing as it is the circumstances under which the drum was insinuated into the story and into the Mompasson household. When Mompasson returned his wife met him at the door and babbled out her fears and frustrations. She told him that for the previous three nights the house had been besieged by thieves and vagabonds trying to break in and wreak their horrible will on her poor unprotected bones. A man's man, Mompasson seized a brace of pistols, cocked them and set out on a systematic search of the house. He found nothing. He was in the middle of suggesting that his wife should take more water with it when he got a taste of what his poor, put-upon spouse, had been enduring.

From all around came the pounding of a giant drum. It was as if the whole house was being beaten and subjected to a military tattoo. As husband, wife and kids huddled together, wide eyed, the sound gradually diminished and faded away. Mompasson wished he hadn't returned so early and fervently hoped that they had just heard the last of it. No such luck. The drumming became wilder and rarely let up. It was so intense now that not only did it make the windows rattle but the vibrations caused solid objects to move about. Mompasson became obsessed with the idea that the cause of the manifestation was the drum he had sequestered at the court and given his children to play with. Sleep being impossible he decided to catch the drum at its devil-inspired labour. He primed a couple of pistols and pulled up a chair and kept a strict watch on the drum – nothing. As dawn approached, the magistrate nodded off. He was jerked awake by the sound of a great howling, like a demented dog, which echoed through the house. Once more the little family huddled together, Mompasson to the fore, his pistols cocked. The cacophony of howling was underscored by the pounding of a giant drum. It seemed to rise from the very fabric of the house. The barrage of noise kept the Mompasson family backed into a corner for a couple of hours. As it began to die away in their immediate vicinity they were aware of noises in other parts of the house. Now the dramatic drumbeats seem to pick up other, less intimidating noises. The sound of horses hooves, a sort of rolling, scampering, marble-scattering sound. As soon as it was light Mompasson called for his carriage and piled his family in it and took them to stay with his brother in Southdown. Three weeks later his wife had the baby they had been expecting and as his servants had reported no new phenomena at his Tedworth home, Mompasson made the decision to return.

Bad move!

As soon as they moved back in the drumming and disturbances began again. Now there appeared to be some form to the banging of the drums. Mompasson recognised several military rallying tattoos and others that were usually played for children. The physical abuse also became more pronounced. There were sounds like nails on a blackboard, which was followed by the children's beds being thrown about. Then chairs started skimming about of their own accord and several people in the household were hit by an assortment of flying objects. Again the family was forced to flee and again, as

soon as they left, the poltergeist activity ceased. Mompasson was now at his wits' end. He was spending so much time moving his family around he wasn't getting any useful time in on the bench sentencing the misguided to hanging or deportation. Determined to settle the hash of his unwelcome, unseen visitor once and for all, he moved back in with his eldest daughter, just ten at the time. Wouldn't you know it? The disturbances started all over again. When it got so bad that he couldn't bear it, he called in a distinguished exorcist who had been responsible for sorting out the problems of many disturbed spirits, the Reverend Joseph Glanville. Glanville had been a supporter, ecclesiastically, of Charles II and had come across many a marauding astral vandal and expected to have no problem settling the hash of a rural psychic troublemaker. He moved into the house and waited patiently for the poltergeist to move out.

It didn't!

Glanville listened and watched, made copious notes and theorised. He began to suspect that the children of the house had more than a little to do with what was going on either consciously or unconsciously. He sat up nights in the children's bedrooms observing them. The disturbances began with a sound like someone scratching on a bare table. It got louder until it almost sounded like the rattle of a kettle drum. The Reverend kept a keen eye on the kids in bed but observed that their hands were resting peacefully on the counterpane and couldn't possibly have contributed to the disturbance. After an hour or two the scratching sound started to shift around the room. Glanville searched everywhere but couldn't find anything to account for the noise. He was still at a loss when the sound appeared to go under the girls' bed and changed to that of a panting dog. The panting got louder and seemed to unleash a physical force, rattling the windows, slamming doors, shaking the house to its foundations. Glanville never got to the bottom of the poltergeist hauntings and left. The Mompasson family grew used to having their nights interrupted by a predecessor of Gene Krupa and became practically blasé about doors being slammed and the house appearing to be about to disintegrate. As quickly as the disturbances started they ceased.

Meanwhile, banged up in a Gloucester goal, the owner of the drum that could probably have been instrumental in unleashing the demons, was boasting that he was responsible for the magistrate and his family having a bad time. He began boasting that he wasn't a good man to cross. As an example of his powers he cited the Mompasson family, which had become quite famous since the Reverend Glanville had put his seal to the haunting. It may have given him great satisfaction to take the kudos for the haunting but he forgot those connected with the law are usually powerful counter-punchers. Mompasson wasn't going to have a lowlife he had put away come back to give him grief. He put it about that the felon didn't only play a drum in a public place without a permit and do indescribable things with sheep but he was also in direct contact with the devil. That did it. Magistrates were big on anything that smacked at a little off-limits necromancy and, before he could get a chance to drum up the devil again, the drummer was hurled into the insalubrious Salisbury goal. He must have had something going for him. Although the grand jury consigned him to the flames he was acquitted by the petty jury. He may have escaped the flames but he didn't escape a fate worse than death – transportation to Australia. Unfortunately his captors weren't as vigilant as you should be when you're guarding a genuine drum banging Satanist and he was able to rap out a command to the wind that the sea couldn't refuse. In the confusion of the resultant shipwreck our drummer was able to escape and after a couple of years turned up in England again.

He didn't forget that Mompasson had been the orchestrator of all his misfortunes and gave him another taste of his devilish drumming for good measure. Nobody had ever been hurt during all the psychic disturbances and the magistrate and his family took the renewed assault philosophically. Probably it was no worse than living under the glide path to Heathrow when Concorde flies in or sitting in a traffic jam in Cromwell Road in the middle of a summer heatwave sharing heavy metal with the occupant of an adjacent convertible.

Another drummer that takes some beating (sorry) is the Cortacky drummer. The object of this ghostly drummer is to spread fear and despondency amongst the Ogilvys by putting it about when one of the clan is about to be separated from his sporran. They brought it on themselves. It seems that back when Old Reekie was merely faintly odorous a messenger arrived with news that the Ogilvys didn't want to hear. The messenger was obviously a moonlighting drummer with a clan band because he had brought his drum with him. An act he was soon made to regret when the waggish Earl of Airlie ordered him to be stuffed into his drum and hurled from the battlements of Cortacky Castle. He was either a very wee Scot or a big-bass drummer. Anyway the drummer wasn't amused and cursed them to listen to his drum forever. It was a good gag – until the ghostly drumming started and presaged Ogilvys dropping like cabers. Before long an Ogilvy couldn't hear a drum without clutching his chest and turning up his toes.

Christmas 1844 was particularly exciting. A Miss Ann Dalrymple came to help out with the new-fangled Christmas tree and mince pies and whatever amusement she could provide for the younger Ogilvys. While she was adjusting her bustle prior to joining the family for Christmas, she heard the sound of music, which was slowly overpowered by the sound of a pounding drum. Later at dinner she ruined the Earl of

Airlie's haggis by asking him who the demented drummer was. Lady Airlie explained the legend but laughed it off. After all she was only an Ogilvy by marriage. Earl Airlie's grin could only be described as sickly. Next morning Dalrymple was awoken by the deadly drummer. She knew that plans were afoot to merge her bloodline with the Ogilvys but decided it wasn't worth it. Before the rest were awake she had packed her bags and scarpered. Lady Airlie died at Brighton, a fashionable resort to die in at this time, six months later. She left a note saying that she knew the drummer had been waiting to take her.

A year later another guest, an Englishman, heard the drums. He was shooting on the grouse moors and heard the distant sound of music. Gradually the music became dominated by the beat of a single drum. The Englishman asked his ghillie what the noise was but he came over all shifty and swore he couldn't hear the drum. Later he found out that his host had left for London where his father, the ninth Earl of Airlie was in a dying state. The Earl duly passed away the following day.

Whether or not the death of the tenth Earl was presaged by the vindictive drummer is open to speculation. He died in the Boer War at the turn of the century and there were so many bangs and explosions, as well as drums and bugles, filling the air that it was hard to tell. Perhaps the malignant spirit went to South Africa to stick it to the Earl, found some sort of identity with the South Africans and stayed. It would explain why the drums have been silent ever since.

36
Highway Ladies

THE JOB DESCRIPTION for women who took to the major roads out of cities in the seventeenth and eighteenth centuries with the expressed purpose of becoming richer, was not the same as for their male counterparts. The highwayman was generally looked on as a free spirit, a cavalier of the road, extracting a toll from the rich and fat and spreading it liberally around the ale houses. He was expected to be romantically inclined towards the ladies and brusque and macho to the men. If time and circumstances permitted and he lifted a skirt or two he was named a rogue but, when eventually he was caught and led to the gallows, he could expect to have an audience of adoring women who wished he had told them to stand and deliver while they could still do him a service. For the Lady of the Road it was different. There weren't many of them for a start. Most ladies found it more comfortable and less dangerous to do their stick-ups in the boudoir. When they did don mask and cloak they tended to be much more businesslike. Their "wham-bang thank-you ma'am" was solely confined to lifting a purse and getting away before they were disturbed. No adventurous nooky with a handsome stranger for them. Having a flintlock poked up his nose was bound to bring on a short-circuited libido for the victim. The other problem with a highway lady was a matter of public perception. It was alright to be deflowered by a butch bloke with a mask on, it was easy to lay back and enjoy the thought of the handsome features underneath. Big, strong, handsome and rough did it everytime. But who wants a woman who comes on like a Japanese sumo wrestler and has to get emotionally involved before she can put out.

There were exceptions.

Lady Katherine Ferrers for one. She was the offspring of Sir Knighton and Lady Katherine Ferrars. As a child she was allowed to run wild. Her father died shortly after Katherine was born and her mother had little interest in the child. She was too busy trying to keep the family home, Markgate Cell, over her head. Markgate Cell had been built originally as a nunnery and was not exactly comfortable. The rooms were basic and unbelievably cold. Nights were often disturbed by off-stage chanting and the occasional spooky manifestation. Lady Katherine, still a handsome and comparatively wealthy woman, soon married again. Her new husband was a Royalist and his social position at that time was none too secure. And he did not exactly splash his wealth around. Lady Katherine had never been a particularly good mother. Her daughter ran wild with the village kids for most of the time and had more in common with her ladyship's gardener than either her or her new husband. But she was reasonably attractive and her free-roaming lifestyle had bred an athleticism and a disregard for convention that, though amusing in a child, didn't make her easy bed fodder on the marriage market. Lady Katherine saw her as an asset. Sir Simon had two sons, both a good deal older than Katherine junior, but still single. Arranged marriages being an acceptable social ploy she soon convinced her husband that a union between their offspring was a financially astute thing to do. Young Katherine, 12-years-old at the time, could only scowl and look enviously at her mates playing in the fields when she was being hitched up to a man twice her age. The nuptials over, Katherine made it very obvious that she would rather play ball than mothers and fathers and avoided her step-brother, now husband, as much as possible.

She had grown up with the son of a local farmer and before her marriage they had been very close. He worked on his father's farm during the day but at night moonlighted as an amateur road agent. Not a very good one. While practising his lack of talent on Finchley Common he was shot. This upset young Katherine. The man she had grown to love had been unfairly executed by her social equals and she wanted revenge – and the excitement that Ralph had told her came with staging a successful moonlight robbery. The old nunnery, Markgate Cell, had a maze of secret rooms and disused passages, as did most houses of any size at this time. One tunnel went from Katherine's bedroom to an outlet well away from the house behind the stables. It had been a favourite haunt of Katherine as a child; now she used it for a more deadly purpose. Her mother had died by now and the new Lady Katherine used the secret place as a hiding place for her mask and pistols as well as any loot she acquired.

Her normal method of robbing her clients were not one usually found in the highwayman's manual. She would hide in a tree above the road and wait for a slowly moving coach or rider to come along – then drop on him, whack him across the head with one of her heavy flintlocks, then make off on her horse on a circuitous route back to Markgate Cell. Although she is best remembered as a highway lady, highway robbery wasn't her only calling. She prided herself that she could turn her hand to any nefarious enterprise. She did a nice little line in cattle rustling and was up for a murder if a bit of

excitement could be guaranteed. Her early life had bred in her a maverick streak that could only be satisfied by a huge dose of adrenalin. She was a junkie's junkie. She didn't need the help of chemical substances to get her high. All she needed was the freedom to create mayhem.

Inevitably, as she became more skilled in her line of work, she became more daring. And probably more relaxed. Lady Katherine was heading for a fall and it came near St Albans. A stupid encounter that had all the earmarks of a put-up job. She saw a lone provisions wagon plodding along a country lane as easy pickings. What she didn't know was that, concealed under a tarpaulin in the back, were a couple of the magistrate's men. Katherine dropped from a tree, casually shot the driver and pulled back the tarpaulin to see what prize she had won for herself. It wasn't what she expected. Two pistols were shoved up her nostrils and she was nicked. Katherine wasn't having that. Her immediate reaction was to drop the cover back over the men and sprint for her faithful stallion. An exceedingly bad move. The bullets easily outran her and she picked up a couple of balls of lead before she could climb into the saddle. She ignored the pain and spurred her horse across the common at a breakneck speed. The pain prevented her from thinking coherently and instead of laying a false trail she made straight for home. The blood loss was horrendous but Lady Katherine managed to make the entrance of her secret tunnel before collapsing. She was dead when the magistrate's men found her. The blood she had lost on her frantic ride had left a trail a blind giraffe could follow.

It was the biggest scandal to hit society since Henry VIII lost his codpiece at the winter ball in Richmond Palace. Katherine's husband was outraged. How could she do this to him? Did she have to come back to Markgate to die? Why couldn't she just fall down where she was shot and court a pauper's lime pit in anonymity?

So incensed was he that he did his best to disassociate his family from her. She was buried secretly and in haste, nobody is sure where, and for years her name was only spoken in whispers.

All her life Lady Katherine had sought excitement and acclaim – even if she remained anonymous. In death she couldn't bear being sidelined so carried on her career as a nighthawk. Travellers along the A5 have reported a cloaked and masked figure, hair loose and flowing out behind, causing near accidents as she gallops along the dark road on her black stallion. Others have testified to being jumped on by an invisible figure as they walk along a nearby lane. Lady Katherine also had it in for the new owners of Markgate Cell. Her ghost has been seen often by the present owners who have developed a sort of uneasy relationship with it. A politeness has grown between them. When they pass on the stairs there is a nod and a mumbled greeting. What Lady Katherine's spirit thinks about it is not easy to discover. It probably didn't help their relationship when the new owner and his wife tried to capture her. Unexpectedly they found themselves on the stairs at either end with the shade of Lady Katherine between them. Unwisely they dived towards the ghost but only found each other.

With all the tales about highwaymen it isn't surprising that several films, from the sublime to the ridiculous in content, have been made about them. At the dramatic end is *The Wicked Lady* (1945) with James Mason and Margaret Lockwood, based on the Lady Katherine Ferrers story. Providing comedy in *Carry On Dick* is Sid James, Barbara Windsor and the Carry-on gang.

The James Mason-Margaret Lockwood film was nicely timed to come out as the war ended. It had a few moustaches bristling and ladies with horsy connections snorting loudly through their nostrils. The story was pretty anodyne. It was Maggie Lockwood's plunging neckline and tight-fitting trousers that were the cause of the outrage. They were much too much for the sensitive American audiences of the time and certain scenes had to be reshot so as not to offend. The script is about this upper-crust lady with a weak, ineffectual husband who has frittered away the family fortune. Frittering away family fortunes took up a lot of screen time back then. Anyway, she decides to get out there and do something about it. In the part of the world that she inhabited there weren't a lot of Lyons' tea shops she could work in so naturally she takes up pistols and mask and becomes a highwayman/lady. Unfortunately she does so on a professional's patch and he doesn't take too kindly to an amateur working his beat and goes after her.

Inevitably he falls for her and as equally inevitably in the moral climate of the day, both come to a sticky end. *Carry On Dick* was just about what you would expect. And we all know who Big Dick is – Sid James.

Michael Winner also had a shot at *The Wicked Lady* in 1983. Not a clever thing to do. There were still those among us who remembered James and Maggie in black and white and we weren't going to be influenced by gaudy colour even if Jack Cardiff was the photographer and made the best of a bad job. There was also the problem of Faye Dunaway's accent. And Alan Bates filling in for gritty James Mason? Come on! What is surprising is that the rather far fetched story on which the film is based is basically true!

37
James Dean – The Little Bastard

HIGHWAYMAN OF a different ilk was heartthrob James Dean. Many stories have been circulated about the pouting star since his dramatic death at the wheel of his sports car. Some say he never took the irrevocable step to the other side but was pulled, badly scarred, from the wreckage and spirited away to a secret hideout to spend the rest of his life in purdah. Presumably with such other legends as Elvis, Lord Lucan, Colin Chapman, Robert Maxwell and Shergar. Another story questions his sexuality – but then anyone who was ever anyone gets their sexuality questioned sooner or later.

Just to be different, it isn't the ghost of Dean that gets the psychic camera clicking but the car he died in. Presumably a car, a thing of metal, rubber and plastic, hasn't got a soul that anyone could shake a stick at. Which means that the extraordinary events that have been connected with the car must be an extension of Dean's ego concentrated in the fabric. That sounds good. Just why James Dean should try to kill or maim anyone who comes within polishing distance of his wrecked car isn't obvious. Could it be that he is so macho he views his automobile as a sex object equivalent to a skittish girlfriend? We'll never know, I guess. What we do know is that James Dean had this thing about cars. Fast cars! He was born in 1931 in Marion, Indiana. Not the most auspicious start for anyone seeking international box-office success probably, but it doesn't seem to have done Dean any harm. By the time he was 24 he was exchanging brooding glances and occasionally body fluids with the stars of the industry like Elizabeth Taylor, Rock Hudson, Raymond Massey, Natalie Wood

and Jim Backus. The film *Rebel Without a Cause* played into his hands with a dramatic "chicken-run" towards a high cliff. His passion for cars, and his determination to be seen as a teenage rebel role model, forced him into a corridor that led directly to a head-on with a Ford Sedan driven by the peculiarly named Donald Turnupseed.

Dean was working on the film *Giant* in 1956. Warner Brothers had specifically warned him against driving in a manner likely to damage his unique body, which they considered their property for the duration of filming. It wasn't a particularly wise thing to do. Dean had already promised himself a day off and entered a car for the Salinas Races at the beginning of October 1956. He didn't have a car that he thought capable of winning the race but this was taken care of when he returned to Los Angeles. He was driving past a car showroom when a silver-grey Porsche Spyder called out to him. He couldn't ignore the call. He made a deal with the company to drive the car under their banner. They would supply the mechanic and look after the race entries. James loved it. It made him a semi-professional driver and added to his image as a tearaway hero. The car was everything he wanted. Before long he was referring to it affectionately as "Little Bastard". As besotted as he was with the car, for some reason it did not find favour with those around him. He was advised to sell it before he killed himself by such diverse friends as Alec Guinness and Ursula Andress. Guinness is reported to have told him that whenever he went near the Little Bastard he had a feeling of impending doom. He was, of course, referring to the car – not the actor.

Dean set out in his Porsche to go to the races. With him he had his mechanic Wetherich and he was followed by an actor friend and photographer from *Collier* magazine, Stan Roth. Roth was there to do a photo-shoot of Dean at the races and, hopefully, mounting the winner's podium. They were in a station wagon and towing a trailer with spare parts, pit-boards and all the paraphernalia needed to service the Little Bastard in the race. Once out on the open road Dean put his foot down and soon out-distanced his supporters. Further along the road James came across a Mercedes-Benz 300SL. It had the fashionable, but shortlived, gull-wing doors and Dean couldn't resist the opportunity of a mini-burn-up. The two cars stopped at a roadhouse and swapped car stories. The driver of the 300SL turned out to be Lance Reventlow, son of Woolworth heiress Barbara Hutton. The stop gave the support car time to catch up and the crew hung around for a while listening to Jimmy and Lance telling exaggerated stories of derring-do on the highway. Lance was also on his way to the races at Salinas and they left promising to meet up the following day.

The next part of the journey took them through the Diablo Mountains. Dean pressed on to Salinas, trying to beat the timetable he had in his head. It was just his bad luck that heading in the opposite direction was a young student on a weekend pass, Gordon Turnupseed. Turnupseed was trying to make a left-hand turn off the highway when Dean breached the rise and bore down on him. He was travelling so fast he gave the youngster no time to work out what to do to avoid a crash. Dean was going too fast to take any effective action and slammed head on into the stalled Ford Sedan.

Dean was killed instantly. The mechanic, Wetherich, was thrown clear and escaped with a broken leg and some minor injuries. Turnupseed was not even taken to hospital. And the Porsche? That was a total write-off, near ripped in two by the force of the crash. Turnupseed was not the most popular man in the world. He was thought of as a cretin who should never have been allowed behind the wheel of a tricycle let alone a powerful car. Whether he could have done anything, other than stay at college that weekend, is debatable. The widespread mourning and theorising came up with a surprising conclusion. The car was in some way cursed. Hadn't all sorts of distinguished people told Dean so before he had even set out on his fatal journey. Usually this sort of knee-jerk reaction dies away after a while but the car seemed to possess a malignant will of its own.

The hauntings started almost before Jimmy Dean was cold. The garage that was called out to remove the Porsche was only a mile or so up the road. But in that short journey the Little Bastard somehow managed to leap off the trailer and break a mechanic's leg. It was dismissed at first as an unfortunate accident. Later events were going to make those with a nose for this sort of thing look at it in a different spectrum when the haunting began in earnest.

The car an insurance write-off, the Barris garage sold off the parts that were untouched by the crash. Two doctors, McHenry and Eschrid, bought the engine and chaindrive and took their cars racing at Pomora, California. First time out, the Little Bastard struck. McHenry died when his car left the track and wrapped itself around a tree. Eschrid's car got out of line and flipped on a corner that wasn't considered difficult. Back at the garage, Barris sold a couple of the tyres of Dean's car to a sports-car fan. The young man was lucky to escape when both tyres exploded simultaneously. The car slewed off the road, jumped a water culvert and stopped only inches away from a death dive over a railway bridge. By now the car was getting a reputation as something to avoid. It didn't deter the souvenir hunters. One young man had his arm ripped open as he tried to have it away with the steering wheel and another nearly lost his eyesight as he was trying to take out one of the bloodstained seats. Barris decided that he had been lucky so far. Nothing had happened to him personally

He wanted to get rid of it but couldn't get a good price. The Californian highway patrol were running a campaign on road crashes – how to prevent them. Barris gave them what remained of the smashed-up Porsche for a gruesome exhibit. In Fresno the Porsche struck again. Stored there overnight, the Little Bastard gave a graphic account of its, or Dean's power. The garage went up in flames. A simple accident? Maybe! The only unusual aspect was that although all the other cars were burned beyond recognition the Little Bastard didn't even get bubbled paintwork. At another display in Sacramento the Porsche again slipped off its stand and claimed a student victim. The jinx on the car was so well established now that nobody wanted to know it. So it was back to Mr Barris. The Little Bastard struck again. The driver lost control of the flat-bed carrying the car and was thrown, uninjured, away from the truck. That wasn't good enough for the Porsche. It leaped off the flat-bed and crushed him to death. The ill-fated car was locked away in the Barris garage. It was too important to be left to rot and two years later, when the incidents that had made it infamous, were almost forgotten, it was on its way to another exhibition. Crossing a motorway the wrecked car somehow managed to free itself and leap over the bridge and onto the freeway below. There was a chain of accidents but the injuries caused by the flying Porsche suddenly appearing in the road were relatively minor. It would seem that a prudent businessman might, at this point, decide to cut his losses and have the ill-fated car scrapped. Barris was made of sterner stuff. Besides, the Dean legend was growing fast and five years after his death his grieving fans had only his death chariot at which to direct their love. Maybe the ghost of Dean, or whatever that haunted the car, was beginning to get tired of the game. At another exhibition in New Orleans, for no apparent reason, the car just fell to pieces. Unlike most supernatural stories the tale of James Dean's Little Bastard has an end that fits its reputation. Coming back from a show in Miami in 1960 the car vanished!

The car's reputation has not declined with the years. It now stands firmly alongside such well known inanimate dealers of death as King Tut's tomb. Or is it the unquiet ghost of Dean that spreads the mayhem? There certainly weren't a lot of Dean's contemporaries still standing before the sixties were out. The actor who had dubbed Dean's voice in several scenes of *Giant,* took an overdose of barbiturates and died. Then his mechanic, Wetherich, was sentenced to life imprisonment for killing his wife. Even Lance Reventlow, who had met Dean only shortly before his fatal crash, was killed flying a plane. Nearly 20 years later the jinx was still operating. Sal Mineo, who had made such an impression in *Rebel Without a Cause,* was stabbed to death in a squalid alley in a lover's quarrel in 1976. Could all those accidents and fatalities be coincidence or is there something in the theory that Dean was in such a highly emotional state when he died that his departing spirit somehow got tangled up with the mangled ironware and struck out indiscriminately at anyone who came into contact with it? And where did the Little Bastard disappear to? Was it the prized catch of some enterprising souvenir hunter or was it called to some automobile purgatory to account for its sins? We will never know. Maybe, just maybe, James Dean wanted to make a film about a devil-possessed car and found his outlet in the movie *Christine* (1983). This is about a restored car that gets an unhealthy crush on its young mechanic, Gordon, who restores her to something of her former glory. Those who don't worship Gordon are done bloodily to death by the rampaging car. Only Gordon is safe until he begins to have thoughts about a feisty woman and puts his mortal limbs in peril from the berserker car.

38

The Dark Cottage – A True Tale for Halloween

It is Hallowe'en and softly, oh so softly, the spirits of the dead
drift past on the Autumn wind.

Old Celtic Saying

ND FINALLY a tale in the true tradition of a gentle ghost story. Wayne Drew is an old friend who has worked forever in the film industry and is a collector of ghost stories. Estate agents claim that after "location, location, location" as the prime reason for buying a property comes atmosphere. They are obviously right. Wayne wallows in the atmosphere of his old house and even more ancient gardens. I believe every word he says. I've sipped champagne in the dark recesses of the garden and eaten dinner on the spot where the disappearing pentagram was carved – and if his house hasn't got at least one resident ghost you can be sure nobody has.

October 31st 1998

It is fast approaching midnight on Hallowe'en. What more appropriate time for a tale of ghosts, dark shadows and things perhaps best left unspoken. As I sit before a blazing applewood fire and listen to the icy winter wind from the bleak Fens, I think back on the strange events of the last few years. This is a true story, but one that is best told by candlelight, as withered leaves rustle and the branches moan, on this the most feared night of the year.

Just over two years ago we finally bought a home in the country. For some considerable time, we had been looking for the right property. Our criteria were, it is true, very demanding. We wanted a period house, within two hours drive of London with original features, in the heart of the country, with a decent-sized garden and at a price that would not bankrupt us. Not an easy task. To be true, what we really wanted was a little piece of magic and ironically I think that we may have got more than we had bargained for.

Magic does not come easy and it comes in many forms. It took us over two years to find it. Each weekend we would set out on Saturday morning and scour the countryside, returning on Sunday evening disappointed and increasingly dispirited. Either the house or the location did not match up. Or else the property was too expensive to consider.

Then in the spring of 1996 we started looking around East Anglia. This is an ancient part of Britain that is made up of Norfolk, Suffolk, Cambridgeshire and Essex. It is a rural, and some would say primitive, area of open landscapes offering stunning vistas and a wonderful unspoilt coastline. It is also rich in history and folklore with mysterious tales of ghosts, phantom dogs and strange lights that haunt the marshes known as the Fens. It was no accident that M.R. James chose this benighted area as the location for many of his classic ghost stories.

After much searching we visited an estate agent in the country town of F– who suggested we should see a property that he felt was perfect for us. At first I told him it was pointless as the house in question was considerably more than we could afford. However he insisted and, with a smile that indicated he knew more than he was prepared to say, we agreed. That is how we came upon our cottage – just by happenstance.

It was early evening, and the sun was getting ready to set in one of those spectacular East Anglian skies whose colours are so remarkable you cannot quite believe them possible. The cottage, the estate agent's literature told us, was situated in the heart of what is known as "high Norfolk": a gently rolling area of countryside in the north-west of the county. It was not particularly easy to find. We drove for miles. Then finally we passed through a small village dominated by a medieval church, crawled down a country lane, then walked along a small track, before it suddenly appeared, its red pantile roof glowing with the rays of the dying sun.

It was truly an ancient cottage. Although it had records going back over 700 years, the estate agent's notes told us, it looked in excellent condition. Surrounded by daffodils, its whitewashed walls were hung thickly with rosebuds and honeysuckle just poised to flower. Adjacent to the house was an ivy-covered barn built to the same design with a high pantile roof in mansard design.

The house was set in a large, richly stocked garden. As well as a fruit garden with apples, peaches, plums, apricots, quinces and many other trees, there was a herb garden, a cottage garden with every type of soft fruit and vegetable imaginable, a large lawn surrounded by trees, a rose garden, a shaded garden covered over with conifers and larches, and a small, densely wooded area with bluebells nestling amongst the ferns. Perhaps, most beautiful of all, on the far side of the cottage, was an old walled garden where more tender plants thrived. Here the house was covered with clematis, the beautiful purple blossoms of wisteria and early flowering creepers.

We looked once more at the estate agent's notes. The cottage was the last house remaining of a deserted village, a village so old that in the Doomsday Book it was referred to as an ancient site. It was built on an early Saxon foundation and had been converted in 1590 when its wood and plaster walls were given a protective shell of brick and the fireplaces installed.

We opened the five-bar gate and approached the house. Crouching beneath the roses, which overhung the front door, we turned the key in the old lock.

We entered first into a small lobby with a cloakroom to the left. The doors were all dark wood and obviously very old. The door to the right led into a heavily beamed dining hall dominated by a large inglenook fireplace. The floors were made up of original pamment tiles and the walls were whitewashed and studded with more oak beams. As well as a small but well-designed kitchen, there was also a lovely sitting room on the ground floor with a further inglenook fireplace, windows that looked out onto the garden on two sides and a door that opened onto the walled garden.

A staircase, ascended from the dining hall, to three good-sized bedrooms, which were also heavily beamed, and a large, modern bathroom. From all the windows there were far-reaching and uninterrupted views over the rolling Norfolk countryside, which stretched to the horizon in every direction.

Well, to make the cliché complete, we fell in love with it at first sight. It was owned by the vicar of a well-known London church and he, for personal reasons, wanted to sell. Literally, within 20 minutes of seeing the house I had phoned him. I explained that I was embarrassed to be making an offer so short of the asking price but to my surprise he did not dismiss it out of hand and invited us both to meet him in London.

In his richly furnished drawing room, built above his church, in one of London's more up-market squares, he explained that the house had already been "sold" to another buyer who had withdrawn before the final exchange of contract. The purchaser had, as a result, been forced to forfeit his deposit and so he was prepared to reduce the asking price. After some small bargaining, our offer, pending structural survey, was made and accepted.

Over the next few weeks we became increasingly anxious. As no-one was prepared to say why the previous purchaser had withdrawn, I was convinced that a major road was planned for the area, that a local farmer was going to build some agricultural monstrosity in the adjacent field or that the house, despite its solid appearance, was just about to fall down. However each search, enquiry and survey revealed that everything was as it should be and that there was no reason for us to have a moment's concern about the property. So in late summer we signed the contract and the cottage became our own.

We moved in immediately. I had taken a two-week vacation so that furniture could be delivered and the house made habitable. This was no easy task as furnishing a period property is more complicated, and expensive, than we imagined. The garden was a riot of colour and it would be difficult to envisage anything more beautiful. The roses that overhung the entrance, the barn and most of the rear wall of the cottage, were in full bloom and their heavily scented petals floated everywhere. It was absolutely idyllic.

Then the problems began ...

First there was the mystery over the documents about the house. When we had been negotiating with the vendor I had been given photocopies of an architectural survey produced by the historical society in Norwich. The day we took up occupancy I found a file containing the "originals" and, to my surprise, discovered that certain lines had been painted over with correcting fluid. I held the back of the document to a mirror and could just make out the phrase "the use of the pentagram is best left to the imagination". Surely a pentagram was a symbol of black magic. The next morning I learned a little more of the house's history from an old lady whom I discovered leaning on the gate. Far from being a friendly soul she looked at me rather fiercely and said without a smile "I'm surprised that you moved in there. Some very strange folk have lived there." She turned out to be our nearest neighbour who had lived, for all her 87 years, in the small cottage at the end of the densely wooded lane that led to our home. Within minutes she had told me that the house was haunted, that it had been owned by a variety of unsavoury characters including a warlock who practised black magic and that one of the previous occupants had gone mad with an axe! Then, after asking me if I had seen "that devil's sign" inscribed on the floor she swiftly turned on her heel and left! A more unusual introduction to the neighbours it would be difficult to imagine.

In the days that passed I was to discover that everything she had told me was true. The house certainly had a reputation in the area: the previous occupant had gone as far as to have the house exorcised and the floor taken up to ensure that nothing "strange" had been buried under it. For "safety's sake" they had also removed the pentagram.

For the first few weeks things seemed fine. But with the onset of autumn the thickening shadows brought with them a definite sense of unease. First it was no more than a "faulty" alarm system, or so it seemed. For some time we were plagued with false burglar alarms; even after the first system was replaced, they continued for a while. All the alarms took place in the same room, the room where the pentagram had been.

Then I began initially to hear, and then to see, "things"!

We can all excuse strange noises in an old house. Boards creek, mice move behind the walls, branches tap the windows. But in the early hours of one morning I awoke to see the figure of a man standing at the end of my bed. He was only there for an instant and then he was gone. To be totally frank, there was nothing frightening about the experience and indeed it could have been nothing more than a mixture of shadows and refracted light. But I had definitely seen the shape of a man. Then, a few days later, I saw another shape on the landing. This time it was smaller and more akin to a shivering movement in the air but, once more, it was definitely a shape. I told no one about these strange occurrences until one day we were visited by some unexpected guests. The children of a previous occupant of the house had been driving in the area and came by on the chance that they could look around the cottage once more. Now in their thirties they were charming people and I invited them in. On several occasions they mentioned that their mother had seen strange things when she had been living there, including unusual lights hovering over the field next to the cottage. This, I was told, had been going on for many years and a previous occupant, in the 1920s, had carved what he had seen into the lintel of the fireplace. (Although his carving had been partially cut away, on examining the beams carefully, I discovered that many had other strange symbols inscribed, some of great age indeed.) They also told me about the pentagram and were surprised that it had been removed from the floor.

It was when we went into my bedroom that I had the biggest surprise. Felix, the brother, asked me if I had "seen anything strange" there. Rather than appear foolish by telling him about my early-morning visitor I said no. He went on to tell me that this was the room where his mother had seen a man standing over the bed and pointed to the exact place where I had seen the shape.

Similarly, on going onto the landing, he said that his sister had seen a boy dressed in blue standing there at the head of the stairs. He was apparently soaking wet and they both believed that he must have drowned in the secluded pond in the wooded area that bordered the house.

The next instalment is the most mysterious to date. In the middle of October last year, we arrived home late in the evening. It was a dark windswept night with thick clouds and only an occasional burst of moonlight. When I opened the front door all was blackness inside. No lights were working and there was the unmistakable smell of sulphur in the air. Carefully I made my way into the dining hall and then the sitting room. It was pitch black and icy cold. From the light of a torch I saw some piles of rubble and some strange black marks on the wall. In our absence, the room, which had once contained the pentagram, had been struck by a thunderbolt. The lightning had penetrated to the centre of what remained of the magical sign.

And that is more or less where the story ends. During the spring and summer months all has been quiet. The cottage has been a relaxing retreat, a private haven that we come to each Friday evening. The weather has been so good that on most days we have eaten beneath the trees. But now that autumn has come I have a feeling that things are about to happen once more. There have been more false burglar alarms – all in the same room.

As the wind rustles the October leaves, and the mists return, I have a strange sense of expectancy. Whatever we encountered on our arrival feels as if it is about to return. Last night, as I sat before the inglenook fire, watching the sparks fly from the glowing logs and listening to the chill wind moaning around the house, I heard a door close and someone walk up the stairs. A common enough sound you might think but I was alone, quite, quite alone in the house.

In such circumstances I need to keep my imagination firmly under control orr else that strange sound in the darkness outside can so easily become the chanting of the long dead warlock, the cackle of the deranged man with the axe, the quiet drip, drip, drip of water from the drowned child – or something far, far worse ...

The Best Ghost Movies

THE THIRTEENTH CHAIR (1929)

The number 13 has been considered unlucky by the superstitious since Jesus asked Judas to pass him the *matzo*. So it is only natural that if you could afford 13 chairs the thirteenth is the one that the business would be done in. It is also natural that a film about this particularly unlucky chair should also be, at the very least, unfortunate. And it appears that this is just what this film is, or was. It seems to have found that repository where unapplauded films end up on a time-locked shelf. Never to see the light of a 40-watt bulb until Edison rises from the grave.

A medium, fainting and timorous, takes on the task of bringing a murderer to book. With a lot of eye make-up and eyeballs that a chameleon would envy, she does the business for lurking law hounds and faces down some carpet-chewing acting to win through. With the help of her spirit guide, she leads the police into a position where they can whip out the old manacles and say "Got you …" only ….

Creaky, and 20 minutes too long – but one for the hyperactive aficionados. Especially as Tod Browning was sharpening his teeth on this one and Bela Lugosi was just a name with a lot of eye make-up.

Producer: MGM
Director: Tod Browning
Writer: Elliott Clawson
Cast: Margaret Wycherly, Bela Lugosi, Holmes Herbert, Leila Hyams
B/W   85 min.

THE THIRTEENTH GUEST (1932)

This was Ginger Rogers' last film outing before she found Fred Astaire. It again capitalises on the number 13 and little else. But Ginger puts some spice into what is a terminally moribund comedy. (I wish I could have resisted saying that). It's another overambitious film. I suppose audiences were more susceptible to sitting for hours in the cinema and not sated by the sofa and television.

Ingredients: a mist-shrouded haunted house, a will to be read at midnight and a young lady with leather lungs that could drown out the sound of the Orient Express at full bore through the Mont Blanc tunnel with all whistles blasting. For black-and-white-movie buffs with insomnia.

Producer: M.H. Hoffman for Monogram
Director: Albert Ray
Writer: Francis Hyland, Arthur Hoerl
DoP: Harry Neumann, Tom Galligan
Cast: Ginger Rogers, Lyle Talbot, J. Farrell MacDonald, James Eagles
B/W   70 min.

THE GHOST WALKS (1934)

About normal for a ghost film of this period. It predates the first of the Topper films by a couple of years but has the usual things to say about extraspectral beings. Dizzy young flappers engage an actor to put a bit of zing in their party by doing some other worldly moaning and chain clanking. Before he can get into the act a real denizen of the dysfunctional dark side appears and scares the living horsehair out of him. Fun with the real ghost, who is mistaken for the actor who is still powering up the nearest inter-state highway. Just the right length. A frame more and the joke would have been on the ghost.

Producer: Chesterfield
Director: Frank Strayer
Writer: Edward T. Lowe
Cast: John Miljan, June Collyer, Richard Carle
B/W   70 min.

THE SCOUNDREL (1935)

This is a real talking-talkie. It seems that no sooner has the film *wunderkind* found how to get vowels and lips in reasonable sync he discovered Noel Coward. Coward was the man to render a telling line unforgettable. Which is probably just as well because the film is not much to look at. There's little movement and the biggest bang in the can is an aircraft crash that goes not with a satisfying kerrumph but with an apologetic yarn. Still it was 1935 and the idea of getting some realism into a film was still some decades away. But who wants realism when naughty Noel is about?

The story starts with a sardonic New York publisher, Anthony Mallare, (Noel Coward) casting lustful looks in the direction of simpering Cora Moore (Julie Haydon) who has eyes only for uptight but faithful Stanley Rudges. But Cora is a budding author and Anthony knows about budding authors. They'll do anything to get their name inscribed on the spine of a book. Accept that Cora won't. Having laid plans to finally separate scribe from true love, Mallare boards a plane bound for Bermuda where sea, sun and playing with his sextant is the order of the day. The phoney aircraft crash has been signalled from the time that Mallare said he was going to go away for a couple of days. The disappointment when the crash happens is softened by the fact that by now you don't care what happens to anyone. The best thing to do is shut your eyes and revel in the sharp and witty lines that trip off the tongues of the lead players and especially that terminal smoothie Coward.

At this point the film borrows heavily from *The Flying Dutchman* legend. Coward's acerbic tongue gets him sent back to earth to find someone who can actually stand being marginalised and condescended to by the labial swordsmen. Eventually he sees the error of his ways and twinkles off to heaven. *The Scoundrel* is not one of the great early talking pictures but it did prove that witty chat and ripe scenery chewing can be entertaining.

Producer: Ben Hecht, Charles MacArthur for Paramount
Director: Ben Hecht, Charles MacArthur
Writer: Ben Hecht, Charles MacArthur
DoP: Lee Garmes
Cast: Noel Coward, Alexander Woolcott, Julie Haydon, Stanley Ridges, Eduardo Glanelli
B/W   74 min.

Robert Donat in a passionate embrace with Jean Parker

THE GHOST GOES WEST (1935)

This was the first English-language film by French whiz-kid René Clair. Murdoch, a Scottish laird (Robert Donat), gets killed and his ghost is trapped in the stones of his castle. Jump a few generations and the latest incumbent laird (also Robert Donat) is about to take a short and uncomfortable visit to Carey St. Enter a brash American, Joe Martin (Eugene Pallette) and his dishy daughter Peggy (Jean Parker). They buy the castle and take it to the States and rebuild. Murdoch is released from being an echo in the stone and not too happy to find himself a displaced apparition. In the end he thaws out and helps his descendent get the girl.

Worth watching. Hammy performances but what can you expect from a film only five years into the "talkie" era?

Producer: Alexander Korda for London Films
Director: René Clair
Writer: Robert E. Sherwood, Geoffrey Kerr
DoP: Harold Rosson
Fx: Ned Mann
Cast: Robert Donat, Jean Parker, Eugene Pallette, Elsa Lanchester, Ralph Bunker, Patricia Hilliard
B/W   85 min.

Cary Grant and Constance Bennett enjoy a dance

TOPPER (1937)

Nicely formed comedy about the dead who refuse to lie down. Bit black bottom and charleston but a good laugh. George and Marion Kirby (Cary Grant and Constance Bennett) just want to live forever and have a good time. A car smash leaves them both dead but chained to earth by the frivolity of their former life. For a while they just continue to have fun spying on their old chums and playing pranks. At last they realise that being dead severely limits their social life and unless they buckle down and make amends they will be spending the rest of eternity switching lights on and off and making mysterious sounds off.

The follow-ups were just daft and predictably the attempt at a series foundered.

Producer: Hal Roach for MGM, Milton H. Bren
Director: Norman Z. McLeod
DoP: Norbert Brodine
From a novel by Thorne Smith
Fx: Roy Seawright
Cast: Constance Bennett, Cary Grant, Roland Young, Billie Burke, Hedda Hopper
B/W   96 min.

Cary Grant and Constance Bennett play the living dead

THE MAN IN THE TRUNK (1942)

This little film is very watchable. Probably because it is short. It touches the right button for a ghost film and it should have left it at that. Unfortunately the director or someone couldn't quite make up his or her mind. Is it just a ghost film based on the premise that souls unexpectedly and abruptly ejected from life are a bit dazed about the hereafter? Instead of sloping off to try on their wings and strum their harp (or pitchfork and cloven hooves if they're heading in the other direction) they hang around trying to be helpful (or not, depending on where they are ultimately heading). So the film is stretched out there in the land of moribund comedy.

A murder victim, very antagonistic towards his assassin and taken with the young assistant DA, makes detecting a cinch by doing all the things ghosts do and there is never a suggestion of a Miranda caution, whatever the terrified punter is blabbing about.

Producer: TCF
Director: Malcolm St Clair
Writer: John Larkin
Cast: Raymond Walburn, Lynne Roberts, J. Carrol Naish
B/W   70 min.

Robert Montgomery as an amateur saxophonist talking to an astral emissary played by Claude Rains

HERE COMES MR JORDAN (1941)

A prize fighter, Robert Montgomery, is killed in an aircraft crash. It turns out that it is all a mistake. The spirit collector, or whatever he's called, played by Edward Horton, is a bit cack-handed and has done his collecting too early. Montgomery has another 40 years before his sell-by date is up. Horton tries to convince Montgomery that it doesn't matter. What's 40 years when you've got eternity. Montgomery doesn't care for that argument – he's a contender. So he pressurises Claude Rains, a sort of smarmy God figure, into letting him return to serve out his sentence. One wee problem. His body has already been incinerated. So Rains gives permission for Montgomery to take on another, recently dead, body. And that bred such follow-up movies as: *Heaven Can Wait*, *The Horn Blows at Midnight*, *That's the Spirit*, *A Matter of Life and Death* and probably dozens that nobody has heard of. It got an Academy award for Best Original Story and nominations for Best Picture, Best Actor and Best Supporting Actor.

Producer: Everett Riskin for Columbia
Director: Alexander Hall
Writer: Harry Segall
DoP: Joe Walker
Cast: Robert Montgomery, Evelyn Keyes, Rita Johnson, Claude Rains, James Gleason, Edward Everett Horton
B/W   93 min.

THE REMARKABLE ANDREW (1942)

The Andrew referred to is the ancient nemesis of the British imperialists – President Jackson. What Old Hickory is doing in a ghost film is a bit tenuous even by Hollywood standards. The story revolves around a young accountant working for City Hall. Someone, somewhere, somehow is having a bit of jiggery-pokery with the books. Young accountant is suspicious. Wants to tell someone but is a bad judge of character. Instead of advice he gets shopped to the gang of crooks running the council and it looks very much as if the rest of his life will be counting bars.

But pretty Ellen Drew is standing by him so it's bound to be alright. But there is too much corruption.

Enter the ghost of Andrew Jackson. He gives a speech that is double talk for war propaganda giving the low-down on the sort of thing that Americans have always fought for, apple pie, Bloomingdales and the American way. Right triumphs over wrong and Jackson is able to return to his marbled hall.

Producer: Richard Blumenthal for Paramount
Director: Stuart Heisler
Writer: Dalton Trumbo
DoP: Theodor Sparkuhl
Cast: William Holden, Ellen Drew, Brian Donlevy, Rod Cameron, Porter Hall
B/W   80 min.

John W. Sublett has an accompanist on the piano

CABIN IN THE SKY (1943)

This is not what you might call a pure, rattling chain and bump in the night ghost story. It is almost a genre on its own. The most recent of this type is the Nicholas Cage offering, *City of Angels*. A story about that little moment, on the cusp of the world of the living and the void of the dead, when anything can happen. As with a lot of movies at that time, it was pinched from the stage and embellished for a wider, less critical audience. As an all-black musical, in an era of fierce racism, it could have died the death but the cast and the music surmounted any racial tension to give 99 minutes of pure musical fantasy from a gang of superstars that it would be hard to come anywhere near to matching today. For black artists in Hollywood it marked a tremendous step forward, although it still insisted on a ghetto background.

It all starts when Little Joe gets severely beaten up and hovers on the brink of death. Waiting to pick over the bones of his life and see if he is fit for hell or heaven are Lucifer junior and God's general. On the Life side are his wife and sweet Georgie Brown. It all gets resolved satisfactorily with a bunch of fantastic numbers by Lena Horne as Georgie Brown and Ethel Waters as the much put-upon wife. Also in there giving their not inconsiderable all, are Duke Ellington and the beaming "Satchmo" Louis Armstrong.

Producer: Arthur Freed for MGM
Director: Vincente Minnelli
Writer: Joseph Schrank
DoP: Sidney Wagner
Music: Roger Edens
Cast: Ethel Waters, Eddie 'Rochester' Anderson, Lena Horne, Louis Armstrong, Rex Ingram
B/W   99 min.

THE UNINVITED (1944)

For me *The Uninvited* is the best ghost film of them all. Recently I was at a Horror Festival in Manchester and it was screened late at night. I was knackered after a heavy day at the coalface but I was determined to see if the film was as good as my memory promised. The last time I saw it was when I was living in West Berlin after the war. It held me spellbound then and I was glad to see that it still had the power to chill to this day. Maybe the sets now look a little too reconstructed and the acting overly mannered but that is a part of screen-life's rich pageantry. It's very difficult to judge the performances of actors from a background dominated by the theatre and compare them with actors whose dramatic moments have to be highlighted by at least one four-letter word. Realism? OK. But if I want realism I'll go to the local and watch 15-year-old kids puking in the car park.

Roderick Fitzgerald (Ray Milland – and there's a name straight off the boards – RF I mean not RM), and sister Pamela (Ruth Hussey in unusually sensitive role), move into a house on the top of a west-country cliff that could be mistaken for Manderley. The smell of mimosa and unaccountable cold areas in the house warn us that something is amiss and we are confirmed in our suspicions when a young girl turns up and introduces herself as Stella Meredith (another name straight from the theatre, Gail Russell). She visits them against the strict orders of that grand old curmudgeon of the early screen, Donald Crisp, who plays the grandfather, Commodore Bench, to the hilt. He tells Roderick that Stella's mum fell to her death from the local lover's leap and he thinks she's after Stella. Roderick, of course, doesn't believe in all that sort of nonsense although he does get a little wall-eyed when fresh flowers wilt in front of his eyes and scary apparitions start appearing. Granddad has had enough. He has Stella banged up in a convenient asylum and cuts off all contact with Roderick. But Roderick isn't sidelined that easily. He figures out there are two ghosts in the house and only one of them is bent on doing Stella a bit of no good. Before the end titles role Roderick has resolved the problem, quieted the unquiet spirits, returned Stella to Granddad, cut himself a little romance, found his sister a boyfriend and mystically turned the dour old house into a haven of light and harmony.

A truly wonderful film and one I will see over and over again. You don't get too many showings these days.

Ruth Hussey and Ray Milland captivated by the scene

Producer: Charles Brackett for Paramount
Director: Lewis Allen
Writer: Dodie Smith
DoP: Charles Lang
Music: Victor Young
Cast: Ray Milland, Ruth Hussey, Gail Russell, Donald Crisp
B/W   98 min.

Danny Kaye and Vera-Ellen on the verge of kissing

WONDER MAN (1945)

Colourful vehicle for Danny Kaye to strut his stuff. He plays the parts of a switched-on zoot-suited nightclub singer and a nerdy, baggy kneed library assistant. Twin Buzzy (singer) gets bumped off by the mob. He wants his doppelgänger brother Edwin (nerd) to take his place and exact revenge on his killers. Just to be helpful Buzzy's ghost takes over Edwin's body at inconvenient moments and the result is a lorra, lorra laughs. Danny also gets a chance to belt out a few of the tongue twisters that made him famous. Funny in the forties. Numbing in the nineties.

Producer: Sam Goldwyn
Director: Bruce Humberstone
DoP: Victor Milner, William Snyder
Writer: Don Hartman, Melville Shavelson, Philip Rapp
Music: Louis Forbes, Ray Heindorf
Cast: Danny Kaye, Virginia Mayo, Vera-Ellen, S.Z. Sakall
Technicolor   97 min.

BLITHE SPIRIT (1945)

This is a film that improves with age. Not because it has anything remotely contemporary to say but because it is basically good humoured. When it was paraded before the first nighters on the West End stage in 1941 it became an instant success. In the middle of a war, with bombs raining down and making death a nightly possibility, it was a relief to see that becoming a ghost had its lighter side. It wasn't an easy time for film-making. Every inch of film was earmarked for aerial reconnaissance. Most of the film crews were in the forces and studios, like Elstree, were either being used as army depots or were turning out propaganda films. In a way *Blithe Spirit* sprang from the loins of a wartime chin lifter. Author Noel Coward and director David Lean had already collaborated on the morale-boosting *In Which We Serve* and *This Happy Breed* before convincing the Ministry of Information that *Blithe Spirit* was a good bet.

The story? It hardly matters. It's the cast and direction that counts. Briefly it is about a writer who doesn't believe in all the claptrap about ghosts and hauntings until a bungling medium conjures up the vindictive shade of his first wife and makes life hell for him. Played with verve and sparkling wit it is still a little gem of the silver screen.

Producer: Anthony Havelock-Allan for Two Cities/Cineguild
Director: David Lean
Writer: Noel Coward
DoP: Ronald Neame
Cast: Rex Harrison, Kay Hammond, Constance Cummings, and Margaret Rutherford as the rare medium.
Technicolor   96 min.

DEAD OF NIGHT (1945)

This is not all ghosts and things that walk through walls but it does hit the squirm spot, which makes the wind breathing down the central-heating ventilator seem a little other worldly. It's a production team film that was one of the best of many churned out in the forties, fifties, sixties and even seventies.

An architect, Walter Craig (Mervyn Jones), turns up to redesign an old house and realises it is the site of a recurring dream he has had for years. Inside the assembled cast are also right out of a nightmare – his. They also claim him as a part of their recurring nightfest and, as is usual in this type of movie, gather round to recount their tales.

And what tales!

The first is told by racing driver Grainger (Antony Baird) who is haunted by a hearse that seems meant exclusively for him. Sally O'Hara (Sally Ann Howes) is dogged by a crying boy who is more than he seems, and Joan Courtland (Googie Withers) has a boyfriend who presents her with a mirror that reflects a rather messy murder that happened to a previous occupant of her boudoir.

The real ghost story is handled by that pair of old British stereotypes, Basil Radford and Naunton Wayne. Both are in lust with the same woman. Radford tricks Wayne into committing suicide then has the inconvenience of having him turn up at his wedding in a semicorporeal form.

The final story features Michael Redgrave being put upon by his ventriloquist dummy. The idea of a dominant dummy has been done to death but of all the offerings over

Hartley Power in conversation with Michael Redgrave's ventriloquist dummy

the years this is the one that would haunt my dreams if I went in for that sort of thing.

Producer: Sidney Cole, John Croydon for Ealing
Director: Cavalcanti, Charles Crichton, Robert Hamer, Basil Dearden
Writer: John Baines, Angus Macphail
DoP: Douglas Slocombe, Stan Pavey
Cast: Mervyn Jones, Roland Culver, Mary Merrall, Miles Malleson, Sally Ann Howes, Michael Redgrave, Basil Radford, Naunton Wayne
B/W   104 min.

Mirror reflection of Googie Withers struggling with her murderer in "The Haunted Mirror" episode

THE REVOLT OF THE GHOSTS (1946)

Although I made a few of them in my time I'm not a great lover of Spanish films. Spanish films in the language sense, I mean. This one is a product of Mexico and that seems to make the difference. Well, I suppose 7,000 miles would.

This film has a plethora of ghosts, famous ghosts at that. Wandering through the old home there is always a chance of bumping into such illustrious apparitions as Don Quixote, Caruso, Napoleon, Chopin, Tutankhamun – you get the picture? Now, those dastardly developers are at it again. They are determined to pull the old house down and build a highrise in its place. This is not looked on with equanimity by the resident shades, who do everything they can in their basically insubstantial powers to obstruct the bulldozers. But Mexican property developers are not easily put off by some eerie piano playing or Egyptian mummies that refuse to stay mum. In the name of progress they raze the old house to the ground and the dispossessed ghosts have to adapt to living in a skyscraper or move into a suburban adobe hut. Very amusing but, if you have to read the sub-titles, forget it.

Producer: Michael Salking for Produccion de Palcules
Director: Adolfo Fernandez Bustamante
Writer: Enrique Castaneda
DoP: Augustin Jimenez
Cast: Amanda Ledesma, Gilbert Roland, Angel Garasa, Luis G. Barreiro, Nelly Monteil
B/W   82 min.

TIME OF THEIR LIVES (1946)

Generally I don't consider myself a fan of smart-mouthed Bud Abbott and Lou Costello films but there are exceptions and this is one of them. Probably because they don't get a chance to bore you to death with one of those "Who's on first base" or "Slowly he turned" routines. In fact the great thing about this film is that, apart from the start, Abbott and Costello are separated by the great divide. The one who caused the cessation of their usual head to heads is Cuthbert (Bud Abbott) who, at the time of the Civil War, fingered Horatio Prim (Lou Costello) as a traitor and deserter. Good, true Horatio's only sin is carelessness. He fell down a well and didn't deliver the message that could have won the battle.

Zoom forward to 1946 and Cuthbert is now Dr Greenway. Up from the well comes the ghost of poor Horatio whom we know so well. He meets up with dishy Melody Allen. There is a really spooky bit of business with Melody. She is called by an ethereal, musical rendering of her name. The two ghosts spend the rest of the film making the doctor's life such hell that by the end you actually feel sorry for him. A first time in an Abbott and Costello film as far as I'm concerned. For some unfathomable reason I have a nostalgic overload for this film and would really like to see it again. But won't. Past experience has warned me never to backtrack – just keep on the fast forward.

Producer: Val Burton for Universal
Director: Charles Barton
DoP: Charles van Enger
Music: Milton Rosen
Cast: Bud Abbott, Lou Costello
B/W   82 min.

THE GHOST AND MRS MUIR (1947)

Wonderfully romantic outing for Rex Harrison, in all his full, sea-booted glory, and Gene Tierney at her serene, china-doll best. If you're widowed and banged up in a little cottage on a craggy cliff-top coastline what more could you want than a resident ghost with corporeal pretensions? Having a precocious eight-year-old Natalie Wood around might be a bit of a hang up but you need a spot of precocity when you have a fractious ghost sparking your mum.

Naturally this is not an easy-going, love-at-first-sight romance. For one thing, Harrison's Captain Daniel Gregg is not exactly ecstatic about the arrival of the strange feminine boarders and tries to put some wind in their sails. But feisty Lucy (Gene Tierney) is having a bad time with her relatives, exemplified by that old smoothy George Sanders who writhes under the *nom de cine* of Mills Fairly, and calls the salty captain out.

The overbearing and grasping relatives haven't got a chance once Lucy has convinced Captain Dan that he would be a lot less dyspeptic if he helped out with the chore of getting rid of the relatives, securing what is rightfully hers and dropping anchor alongside her moorings.

This isn't a big story. More a gentle poem with a few basso profundo asides but it gets an A plus for entertainment and valour. Obviously once was not enough and eight years later a remake, scheduled to sink quicker than the *Titanic*, tried to rekindle the magic and was only slightly less mawkish and banal than the TV series that followed.

Producer: Fred Kohlmar for TCF
Director: Joseph L. Mankiewicz
Writer: Philip Dunne
DoP: Charles Lang
Music: Bernard Herrmann
Cast: Gene Tierney, Rex Harrison, George Sanders, Natalie Wood
B/W   104 min.

Delicate Gene Tierney falls in love with the ghost of sea-captain, Rex Harrison

THE GHOSTS OF BERKELEY SQUARE (1947)

The main memory the survivors of this bit of first world war whimsy is of the skeletal Felix Aylmer, in smoking cap and dressing gown trying to be reassuring. Robert Morley, a man who I believe has never been young, huffs and puffs and does a great imitation of someone who wants to be somewhere else.

The eighteenth-century ghosts are in an ethereal time lock. Never to be free to pass on to better things until royalty visits the house. Which probably means that they will spend eternity giving the various owners a turn or looking longingly out of the window and giving passers-by a turn. Until just before the credits are run. An obliging member of royalty turns up and the unquiet spirits are quietened.

Producer: Louis H. Jackson for British National
Director: Vernon Sewell
Writer: James Seymour
DoP: Ernest Palmer
Cast: Felix Aylmer, Robert Morley, Yvonne Arnaud, Wilfrid Hyde White
B/W   89 min.

Jennifer Jones and Joseph Cotten share the view from Brooklyn Bridge

PORTRAIT OF JENNIE (1948)

If there is such a thing as serial ghosts, Jennie (Jennifer Jones) is it. Real spooky with the looks of a fully paid-up member of the Ethereal Spirit Union on stand-by for Central Casting. Story is a little dotty but the strong cast led by Joseph Cotten as a not-too-good artist (Adam Adams) who finds his muse only to lose her just when he is getting his stuff together, is strengthened by director William Dieterle's deft touch and helps the audience suspend reality.

Adam Adams, is a painter of insipid watercolours, doesn't do much until Jennie turns up in Central Park

as he sits contemplating the holes in his shoes. She tells him a story about being a convent girl, sings him a brief operatic aria and leaves. Just a normal day in Central Park you might think. But from then on Adam's luck changes. Doted on by an elderly patroness with more schlock than artistic appreciation, Miss Spinner (Ethel Barrymore), buys up his work and sees him all right for a buck or two.

Then Jennie turns up again. She looks a lot older but Adams doesn't care. He's now moonlighting in a café painting murals on the wall for a fistful of dollars and all the salami on rye he can get his gnashers around. Naturally he wants to paint a portrait of Jennie or the film would have had to look for another title. By now he has begun to notice that Jennie's accelerated ageing process is a little extraordinary. When Miss Spinner sees the portrait she flips. This puts Adams into a new category – a master! Adams agrees totally. But Jennie has vanished.

Desperate to milk what publicity he can from presenting his model to his adoring public, he searches frantically for her. At the convent he meets Lillian Gish doubling as a suitably fey Mother Superior and learns that Jennie died in a New England hurricane 12 years earlier. Adam belts off to New England. It is the anniversary of Jennie's death. And, of course, there is a reprise of the hurricane that killed her. Jennie comes to him, young and in all her spiritual glory, and tells him that their love will last for all eternity. Adams looks as if a little carnal love on account might be acceptable but before he can spoil a beautiful moment, Jennie vanishes never to return.

Adams thinks it has all been a lovely illusion until he finds Jennie's handkerchief in his pocket and realises that his true love is waiting for him in the afterlife. He goes back to his painting, secure in the knowledge that he has been touched by a little bit of heaven.

And so have the wet-eyed audience.

Producer: David O. Selznick for Vanguard
Director: William Dieterle
Writer: Peter Berneis, Paul Osborn, Leonard Bernovici
DoP: Joseph August
Music: Dimitri Tiomkin
Cast: Joseph Cotten, Jennifer Jones, Ethel Barrymore, Lillian Gish
B/W (tinted sequence)   86 min.

Margarita d'Alvarez connects James Mason with the disaster that lies in the fortune cards for her son

PANDORA AND THE FLYING DUTCHMAN (1950)

The *Flying Dutchman* has been given an airing in most forms of entertainment. From books through to operas and films with sober sightings anywhere from the Cape of Good Hope to the North Sea.

Memorable forties' heart-throbs James Mason and Ava Gardner took the phantom ship on a filmic cruise in 1951 and came up with a tear-jerker that almost sank her. Mason, as the captain doomed to sail the seas forever unless a woman is willing to sacrifice her all for him, scowls and pouts pettishly but finally comes up with the goods.

Ava, as his salvation, doesn't seem to be that keen on setting sail with Mason either for the sake of the story or to brew up some chemistry between them. One of those films that would have been enhanced by being filmed in black and white. The colour, at least on the copy I saw, was awful.

Producer: Albert Lewin for Romulus
Director: Albert Lewin
Writer: Albert Lewin
DoP: Jack Cardiff
Music: Alan Rawshorne
Cast: James Mason, Ava Gardner, Nigel Patrick,
Marius Goring
Technicolor   122 min.

THE GHOST SHIP (1952)

Great afternoon film, this. All jut-jawed ex-naval officers and simpering women in print frocks and silly hats. Very much a "let's forget the war and show how we've progressed" film. The hang up with the military past and the dividing line between officers and the ranks is very much in evidence. Well, it was seven years after the war and England had only just given up rationing. What is good about this film is that you're never sure whether there is a genuinely malevolent presence on board or whether it is someone just trying to scare off the bright-eyed couple who have sunk their entire life savings into buying and renovating the ship!

And for one blissful time it doesn't turn out to be some psychologically crippled cousin trying to claim what he thinks is rightfully his.

Producer: Anglo Amalgamated
Director: Vernon Sewell
Writer: Vernon Sewell
Cast: Dermot Walsh, Hazel Court, Hugh Burden
B/W   74 min.

THIRTEEN GHOSTS (1960)

The opportunities opened up by the ghost story seem to be limitless. Why then do the stories that manifest themselves onto the screen appear more insubstantial than the entity they exhibit? Haunted houses, screaming ingenues, butlers breathing bad breath and a propensity for characters to wander off by themselves seems to be the limit of a ghost-story producer: or director's imagination. This film, again overlong for such a fragile story, relies on gimmicks to bolster up its tired theme. But then the director and producer: in question is William Castle. Although shot mainly in black and white, Bill probably found that he had some cash to spare or some time-expired colour stock and shoved in a couple of colour sequences. He also handed out anaglyphic glasses so that you could put the spectre in the picture yourself. The best thing about these was you could juice up something like *The Sound of Music* by having Julie Andrews goosed by your very own spectre.

Producer: William Castle for Columbia
Director: William Castle
Writer: Robb White
DoP: Joseph Biroc
Cast: Charles Herbert, Jo Morrow, Martin Milner, Rosemary de Camp
B/W (colour sequence)   88 min.

HOUSE ON HAUNTED HILL (1958)

Whenever this film is written about it is usually dismissed as a bit of a cop-out. For some reason the fact that it is tied in through the producer: to such films as *Thirteen Ghosts*, *The Tingler* and *Macabre* seems to give the green light to be decidedly sniffy. But taking into account the sort of films that were taking up screen space in the late fifties it definitely has a certain something. And it's not the script or the basic story. It revolves around a millionaire laying on a party in an old house that would kill the party spirit as soon as the doorbell chimes. The guests who turn up are obviously on call from central casting and have practised their art in one of the dozen or so films that were made about that time.

Most of the film doesn't hang together and the "*I'll just pop off to some darkened room where nobody else can find me*" syndrome is well to the fore. But for all of that the film carries you along and it is only after you have seen it that you come over all sophisticated and disclaim any involvement in the decidedly shaky atmosphere it builds up.

It was directed by William Castle who was an actor until he bought a light meter and went on the other side of the camera. Many of his pictures had that added element that bordered on farce but played so earnestly you didn't like to laugh. It all came out when there was a concentrated effort on the part of film producer:s to get the customers into the cinema. That was what 3D was all about. Get the bums on seats ducking and diving and they would be back for more. Then they went into curious noises off and flashing lights on the screen to warn you that Vincent Price was about to do something that would seem perfectly normal in a comedy now. Castle's contribution was free life-insurance policies, tingling seats and a luminescent skeleton doing swan dives over the one and ninepennies.

Producer: William Castle for Allied Artists
Director: William Castle
Writer: Robb White
DoP: Carl Guthrie
Music: Von Dexter
Cast: Vincent Price, Richard Long, Carol Ohmart, Elisha Cook Junior
B/W   75 min.

CHE INNOCENTS (1961)

Deborah Kerr's performances are always wonderful.
Her strength is playing an innocent, well-brought up
young gel who doesn't quite know what is going on but
has hidden depths. In this film she adds another
dimension – a sort of menace. Why that should be
when she is the menacee and not the menacer I don't
know. Maybe it is just me but all through the film I felt
there was more to her than there turned out to be.

Deborah, reprising the Siam role of governess arrives
at a grand old country manor to look after the children.
Well, one child actually but there is the feeling that
there is a second one present. Miss Giddens (Kerr), is
enchanted by her young charge, Flora (Pamela
Franklin) although the audience soon cottons onto the
fact that she is not the little angel she makes out to be.
Then Master Miles (Martin Stephens) gets expelled
from school and arrives home and into the loving care
of Miss Giddens. She's still in the stage of being
enchanted and soon falls under the young master's
spell. Then she sees a man on the roof. When she goes
to investigate she finds Miles there feeding the pigeons.
He tells her she is mistaken: no-one has been on the
roof since he arrived and he has been there for hours.

Miss Giddens decides she has got to start taking
more water in her cough syrup but then has a nasty turn
when she sees a woman pressing her nose to her
bedroom window. Her scream gets the attention of the
household but, predictably, when they investigate they
find no-one. A further encounter with a man with the
sort of face that a surfeit of crab nightmares is made of,
gets Giddens into a state of super-agitation and she
confides in the housekeeper, Mrs Grose (Megs
Jenkins). She does a lot of significant looking and
oohing and aahing and makes the governess feel better
by claiming that she's not the only one to have seen the
apparitions. They fit the description of the farm
manager and his mistress who, incidentally, was the
governess before Giddens. She hints that there was a
little bit of nastiness involving the children. Giddens
now undergoes a number of horrid experiences before
sorting the children out and living happily ever after.
Or do they?

There is enough eeriness and off-the-wall happenings
to keep anyone interested in apparitions with nasty
habits happy.

*A determined Deborah Kerr with her young charge
Pamela Franklin*

Producer: Jack Clayton for TCF/Achilles
Director: Jack Clayton
Writer: William Archibald, Truman Capote, John
  Mortimer
DoP: Freddie Francis
Cast: Deborah Kerr, Michael Redgrave, Peter
  Wyngarde, Megs Jenkins, Martin Stephens, Pamela
  Franklin
B/W (Cinemascope)   99 min.

*Deborah Kerr with Martin Stephens in
the moonlit garden*

THE HAUNTING (1963)

This is another film that it is difficult to claim as a hand on pulsating heart ghost movie. But then again …. Ghosts, elementals, poltergeists and just a surfeit of camembert seem to want to creep in under the ghost banner. Even eponymous Harvey, the unseen companion of Jimmy Stewart, is sometimes roughly shovelled into the ghost patch. *The Haunting* is not a film to try and focus your pupils on after a heavy night at the office. For one thing, director Robert Wise seems to have developed leg trouble in his tripod. Smack my wrist if I'm wrong but I don't think there are more than a handful of straight horizontal shots in the whole film. Is that bad? I think it can be overdone. But it does get across that it is the house that has jumped the cogs of rationality, helped by that wonderful standby for anything spooky or a bit off centre, Rosalie Crutchley.

If you are looking for an update on Bob Hope's *Cat and the Canary*, forget it. There's not a joke, a nudge or even a half-wink in this one. Which is curious because the plot is very similar. Bloke inherits house, finds it haunted, calls in the experts. That's when the trouble really starts. Like all good horror directors Wise understands that once the ogre in the cupboard is let out it is time to go home. So he keeps his ghost, ghoul or elemental off-screen but super-audible and violent.

In the end I put it all down to our own dear Richard Johnson who, as Dr Medway, is tampering with the extremes of ESP. Helping him out with the paranormal claptrap is Julie Harris (Eleanor) and the icy Claire Bloom. Julie and Claire carry on a sub-lesbian relationship helped out by the maniacal house, and the owner, Russ Tamblyn (Luke Sanderson) flits between boyish charm, jut-jawed heroism and a need to be elsewhere explaining what has happened to his career.

Producer: Robert Wise for MGM/Argyle
Director: Robert Wise
Writer: Nelson Gidding
DoP: David Boulton
Cast: Julie Harris, Claire Bloom, Richard Johnson,
 Russ Tamblyn, Rosalie Crutchley
B/W (Panavision) 112 min.

A terrified Julie Harris with her back to the wall

JULIET OF THE SPIRITS (1965)

This is an interesting if not exactly ghost-based film. Probably the most interesting thing about it is that it is the first time Federico Fellini moved out of the moody black and white into more festive colour. The ghosts appear at a seance the eponymous Juliet (Giulietta Masina) holds to try and get a line on her lying, two-timing husband, Giorgio (Mario Pisu). The omens are bad. So plucky Juliet hires a gumshoe to get the low-down on Giorgio's extra-marital activities. She finds out that her boring old husband is putting it about more than a little and decides it is payback time. Juliet doesn't come out of it very well. She seems to think that the proper way to act comes from the characters in graphic novels and soap operas. Fellini made the visuals stunning but after you've watched shadows on a wall and studied the wrinkled brows for a while you want them to get on with it. Later Fellini may be harder to understand but it does keep your interest.

Producer: Clemente Fracassi for Federiz/Francoriz
Director: Federico Fellini
Writer: Federico Fellini, Tullio Pinnelli, Brunello Rondi, Ennio Flaiano
DoP: Gianna de Venanzo
Cast: Giulietta Masina, Mario Pisu, Sandra Milo
Technicolor   145 min.

Fellini attends to detail in another stunning shot

Sandra Milo's grand finale as the circus ballerina

THE SPIRIT IS WILLING (1966)

Another spectral outing for the indefatigable auteur William Castle. It suffers from the same bug that gnaws at all these films. It is as if the company sits around and somebody says brightly, "Let's make a ghost film!" Then the director says "Oh yes, what a capital idea. You can play the woman who knows but says nowt and you …"

Then he has the cartoon bulb click on in his head and he says, "And we'll play if for laughs ... and ... and ... we'll do something different!"

Then he proceeds to make a remake of a remake and so on ad infinitum.

The amazing gimmick in this one revolves around a family holiday in a haunted house. That's it!

Producer: William Castle for Paramount
Director: William Castle
Writer: Ben Starr
DoP: Hal Stine
Cast: Sid Caesar, Vera Miles, John McGiver, Cass Daley, John Astin
Technicolor   100 min.

BLACKBEARD'S GHOST (1967)

This is a film that was tailored for Peter Ustinov at his best – before someone told him that he was the best raconteur in the world and he felt that he had to spend his life proving it. He did have some help. The end of Disney's rainbow for a start. Then there is Suzanne Pleshette and hunky Dean Jones. They all stoke up the magic of a group of dedicated do-gooders who want to stop their favourite hotel being redesigned as a haven for gamblers. But without doubt it is Ustinov's film. He's the shade of the old pirate who roamed the West Indies, burning, looting, raping and generally being laddish. He was finally done in by the Brits. What happened to him after that is anyone's guess.

This version says he had a complete character change and became a champion of distressed wimps. Pity he doesn't get a few of them to walk the plank but concentrates on the baddies instead.

Very enjoyable and it takes a refreshingly new look at the ghost story although its whimsical nature separates it from the draped sheet and the rattling chains and casts it into a sort of entertainment limbo.

Producer: Bill Walsh for Walt Disney
Director: Robert Stevenson
Writer: Bill Walsh, Don Da Gradi
DoP: Edward Colman
Cast: Peter Ustinov, Suzanne Pleshette, Dean Jones
Technicolor   107 min.

THE HOUR OF THE WOLF (1968)

Ingmar Bergman got together a cast of outstanding actors, threw them this screenplay and told them to get on with it. Which wasn't the easiest thing in the world to do considering that Ingmar was directing and had written the script. There was a bit of desperation about Ingmar's thoughts on what, exactly, he wanted. The script had been around for quite a while and had been in and out of the starting blocks more often than a 100-yard sprinter. All Bergman knew was he wanted something gothic and confusing and got Max von Sydow and Liv Ullman to deliver the goods for him.

Johan Borg (von Sydow) has the highly original idea of taking his pregnant wife Alma (Liv Ullman) to an island where conditions are decidedly primitive. From the moment they set foot to shingle, strange things start to happen. Both of them see apparitions and experience feelings that they would rather have left locked away in their disconnected synaptic web. Johan has encounters that make even his lugubrious face look more doleful. There's a pretty boy that has Johan thinking dark thoughts. Then he finds a ghost that can walk nonchalantly up the wall. He nearly follows him when he meets a woman who rips off her face just to confirm some deep psychological trauma he has about women.

Meanwhile Alma is having an equally Gothic experience with a ghost who enigmatically recommends Johan's diaries as suitable bedtime reading for a highly susceptible pregnant woman. After minimal resistance, a lot of haunted looks and maximum suspense, Alma reads his diaries and ruins her life.

A gripping film, slow, as only Bergman can be and get away with it, but the chillier moments are glacial and the haunting, depressing atmosphere is never far away. The film should not be seen in a negative mood.

Producer: Lars-Owe Carlberg for Svensk Filmindustri
Director: Ingmar Bergman
Writer: Ingmar Bergman
DoP: Sven Nykvist
Music: Lars Johan Werle, Mozart and Johann Sebastian
  Bach
Cast: Liv Ullman, Max von Sydow
B/W   89 min.

Marley's Ghost (Alec Guinness) greets Scrooge on his arrival in Hell

SCROOGE (1970)

Charles Dickens' bestseller has been filmed so many times without a really outstanding version shining out of the dross that it is difficult to pick one as the more or less definitive version. 1908 saw a version put out by Essenay. Two years later Edison got into the act. 1913 Seymour Hicks had a go at it and then reprised it in 1935. Rupert Julian also had a couple of bites at it in 1916 and 1938. The war with its rationing put a block on "biggest turkeys" in the city for a while, then Alastair Sim had a crack at it in 1951. A musical starring Albert Finney followed in 1970 and George C.

Scott was a corpulent Scrooge in a TV film in 1984. Michael Caine also had a go at it with the Muppets but the less said about that the better.

Producer: Robert H. Solo for Cinema
   Center/Waterbury
Director: Ronald Neame
Writer: Leslie Bricusse
DoP: Oswald Morris
Cast: Albert Finney, Michael Medwin, Alec Guinness,
   Edith Evans, Kenneth More, David Collings
Technicolor   113 min.

MACBETH (1972)

This is the Scottish play as William himself might have filmed it if a camera, film stock and a casting couch had been available to him in the early seventeenth century. Riotous colours, bags of swagger and deafening sound. And the bonus of Francesca Annis in the buff. I would have given a good deal of buffiness to get that part. Hugh Hefner, the big daddy of the Playboy set, had half-promised it to me after viewing *The Vampire Lovers*. Well, maybe "half-promised" is a bit strong. He actually said "I could see you as Lady Macbeth." He was the money behind the film and probably said that to all the girls. Tuesday Weld was originally cast but balked at giving her all for the sake of art so at least the part was still on the cards for all us hopefuls. And I had been quite friendly with Sharon Tate – the wife of director Roman Polanski, murdered by the Manson gang – another qualification I deemed worthy of the part. But that's just how actors think and the role went to Francesca and she did a great job with it. However …

This is the latest in a string of Macbeths going back to the silent days. Most of them came straight off the stage and brought scenery chewing to a fine art. The usual inept act of desecration, playing it in modern dress, turned out to be not so terrible in the 1956 *Joe Macbeth* starring Paul Douglas. Even the Japanese didn't exactly make a fist of it in *The Throne of Blood*. Which proves, if proof were necessary, that you can't keep a good story off the best-selling shelf. The common denominator in all of them was the scene where Macbeth is confronted with the ghost of the murdered Banquo and does his nut. Classically in the earlier films, hysterically in the later. It must be admitted that it could be a bit off-putting having the ghost of the bloke you have just paid good gelt to his murderer for dispatching, sitting in your chair shaking his gory locks at you.

Producer: Andrew Braunsberg for Playboy/Caliban
Director: Roman Polanski
Writer: Roman Polanski, Kenneth Tynan
DoP: Gilbert Taylor
Cast: Jon Finch, Francesca Annis, Martin Shaw, Nicholas Selby
Technicolor Todd-AO 35   140 min.

Jon Finch at arms as Macbeth

Julie Christie, Hilary Mason and Clelia Matania in a funeral barge on the Canale Grande

DON'T LOOK NOW (1973)

In recent years this film has been opened up to a lot of ill-conceived criticism. I'm not sure why. Maybe it is a little long and repetitive but, for atmosphere and the shiver down the spine, it is hard to beat. When it was released it was put out on a double bill with a film I did called *The Wicker Man* that has become one of the most heralded classic movies of the British horror genre.

The story is set in a crumbling Venice where John Baxter, with his wife, has been brought in to try and save some of the choicier bits of Venetian architecture from sinking into the sewers. Baxter is grateful for the distraction. Shortly before, his five-year-old daughter has been drowned in a garden pond. At the time she was wearing a bright red hooded coat. Ma and Pa had been indulging in some good old fashioned rumpy-pumpy at the time. They blame themselves for letting carnal pleasure come between them and their duty as parents.

In Venice they are initially a lot happier. But not for long. Baxter keeps seeing this little red-clad figure, that he is convinced is the ghost of his daughter. His wife is also having a bad time. A couple of ghoulish sisters, one blind and psychic, the other hostile and menacing, seem set upon driving her out of what is left of her mind.

Out on the canal they see the two sisters in a funeral barge. There seems to be no particular menace to them or their lives but the Baxters are operating on a different emotional plane to the rest of us and it tips them over the edge. When next Baxter sees the red-clad figure he sets out after it, determined to bring the whole regrettable incident to an end.

He does that alright. The red coat turns out to be a maniacal dwarf and she stabs him to death. Sad really. It was all going so well up until then.

Producer: Peter Katz for British Lion/Casey/Eldorado
Director: Nicolas Roeg
Writer: Allan Scott, Chris Bryant
(Based on a story by Daphne du Maurier)
DoP: Anthony Richmond
Music: Pino Donaggio
Cast: Donald Sutherland, Julie Christie, Hillary
 Mason, Clelia Matania
Technicolor 110 mins.

Joe Pendleton (Warren Beatty) discussing his unusual situation with Heaven's emissary Mr Jordan (James Mason)

ḤEAVEN CAN WAIT (1978)

When is a ghost not a ghost? For instance: Warren Beatty is driving along a road and has an accident. When he turns up in heaven the recording angel gets in a bit of a tizzy because he is not expected, his sheets haven't been turned back and his harp is far from being properly tuned. Fortunately for his inefficient messenger of death, Beatty's character, Joe Pendleton, is an all-American footballer and a little thing like premature death doesn't faze him. He demands that the boss angel, Mr Jordan, played at his silky best by James Mason, should allow him to return to play out his season amongst the cheerleaders and popcorn

vendors. A slight problem is that his body has already been through the funeral pyre and he doesn't fancy spending eternity in a jar on anyone's mantelpiece.

Pendleton hi-jacks a body recently murdered by Dyan Cannon, a nutter if ever there was one, who understandably can't get her head around the fact that the husband she has so recently butchered, is back in the family circle. So far, so good. The rest is a trifle hard to swallow. The newly bodied Beatty now wants to play in the Super Bowl. He enlists the aid of his old coach, played in some confusion by Jack Warden, and gets back in some sort of shape.

The film is a remake of the 1941 *Here Comes Mr Jordan*. It's not bad – just a bit uninvolving. It was always going to be compared detrimentally to the forties film and Beatty's reputation, rightly or wrongly deserved, put off the punters. But is it a genuine ghost film – ah! There's the rub.

Producer: Howard W. Koch Junior, Charles H.
 McGuire for Paramount/Warren Beatty
Director: Warren Beatty, Buck Henry
Writer: Warren Beatty, Elaine May
DoP: William A. Fraker
Cast: Warren Beatty, Julie Christie, James Mason,
 Dyan Cannon, Jack Warden
Movielab   110 min.

Warren Beatty entertaining Julie Christie with a little musical session in the park

THE AMITYVILLE HORROR (1979)

Claimed to be based on events that happened in Amityville when the Lutz family, James Brolin, Margot Kidder and kids, moved into a derelict house that was the scene of a macabre multimurder. Did fantastic business and spawned all sort of lesser horrors. Everything is thrown into the cauldron – demons, ghouls, ghosts, elementals, flies, gunge and Rod Steiger. Off-screen it all ended with everybody who had anything to do with the film suing each other. Thankfully it has now been left alone.

Producer: Ronald Saland, Elliot Geisinger for
   AIP/Cinema 77
Director: Stuart Rosenberg
Writer: Sandor Stern
DoP: Fred J. Koenekamp
Fx: Delwyn Rheaume
Cast: James Brolin, Rod Steiger, Margot Kidder, Movielab   118 min.

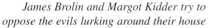

*James Brolin is determined to
defend himself against any evil*

*James Brolin and Margot Kidder try to
oppose the evils lurking around their house*

SOMEWHERE IN TIME (1980)

A real weepy this. It was Christopher Reeve's chance to cast aside the swirling cape, pull his trousers up over his Y-fronts and perform. He almost did it, too! Just that you expected him at any time to find a nineteenth-century alternative to a phone box and whip off his brown Derby and tight pants and reverse his fate by flying around the world and turning the clock forward – or backward – clock to suit his precarious situation.

Steve goes back in time and falls in love with Jane Seymour. Problem is that he can't stay in the given time slot and make a happy-ever-after a certainty. Jane provides a great motivation and drives poor old Steve mad with desire and downright logistical frustration. It works up to a real three-man-size-tissue ending – then spoils it. Nevertheless it's worth seeing. Jane has never been lovelier and if you can block out the ghostly apparition of the man from Krypton, Reeves is great. But is it a ghost story? Well …

Basically it's a remake of the 1933 *Berkeley Square* made by the father of Hollywood, Jesse Lasky, with the fragile Leslie Howard playing the Reeves part and penned by Dracula writer John Balderston. I was also reminded of *I'll Never Forget You*.

Producer: Stephen Deutsch for Universal/Rastar
Director: Jeannot Szwarc
Writer: Richard Matheson
DoP: Isidore Mankofsky
Music: John Barry
Cast: Christopher Reeve, Jane Seymour, Christopher Plummer
Technicolor   104 min.

CHRISTINE (1983)

It's a good job that the car in this movie is regenerative. Can you imagine the scepticism of an insurance assessor when a claim form came in saying that the incineration of the vehicle was due to it being out on its own at the time and having a disagreement with a garage mechanic. Oh yes! Everyone in the garage was killed and the building's surrounding area devastated. Or how about trying to explain how the wings and side panels were ripped off because the car was trying to compact someone who had upset you?

Christine, the movie, comes into that grey area where there seems to be a ghostly presence but sharpens up the definition between the varying aspects of the supernatural. While it is never stated that the car is inhabited by the ghost of a living person, there is dialogue that makes you believe that ultimately that is what they are getting at. Why, for instance, should the car, Christine, get the hots for the nerd who renovates her if her innards are not motivated by something more sexually stimulating than a fuel pump and a water radiator?

But then, of course, there is James Dean's Little Bastard. So maybe Christine is a real ghost story after all.

Christine 2 should be about a flashy, beautifully painted woman with pneumatic suspension and a fast lifestyle with the hots for a Jaguar XK120.

Producer: Richard Kobritz for Columbia/Delphi
Director: John Carpenter
Writer: Bill Phillips
DoP: Donald M. Morgan
Cast: John Stockwell, Alexandra Paul, Harry Dean Stanton
Technicolor   110 mins.

Bill Murray, Dan Aykroyd and Harold Ramis, costumed as Ghostbusters, pose with their ghost-fighting equipment

GHOSTBUSTERS (1984)

What can I say about this film? For one thing, it seems the title is a bit of a misnomer. Whatever the lads are after, they have very little to do with your staid white wraith, chain-clanking, country-house apparition. The slimy, fast-moving elementals seem to be there to perpetuate the custard-pie syndrome and splurge at regular intervals over the gormless but intermittently savant hunters. The idea of sucking in the elementals with a super vacuum cleaner is a cute idea but gets a bit repetitive without pushing the story on to something to get your wisdom teeth masticating on.

Sigourney Weaver, as a classical cellist with an apartment built as competition to Grand Central Station, and a refrigerator from hell, uses restrained sex appeal and seduces lead buster Bill Murrey (Dr Peter Vankman) into taking on her case. Her case is that she is inconveniently living in the portal about to be used by the Sumerian devil who also doubles as a gargoyle.

The Ghostbusters, Murray, Dan Aykroyd (Dr Raymond Stantz) Harold Ramis (Dr Egon Spenler)

,demolish a lot of New York dealing with their unworldly infestation and most folk would probably opt for keeping the elementals. At least until the Sumerian devil turns up and intends to have his wicked way with raunchy Sigourney. Murray proves that love conquers all, at least until the less than satisfactory sequel in 1989, and Central Park goes back to being a place where your average mugger can go about his business unmolested by malignant green slime.

And after all that there's not a down-to-earth, soul-tortured wraith in sight.

Producer: Ivan Reitman for Columbia/Delphi
Director: Ivan Reitman
Writer: Dan Aykroyd, Harold Ramis
DoP: Laszlo Kovacs, Herb Wagreitch
Music: Elmer Bernstein
Sfx: Richard Edlund
Cast: Bill Murray, Dan Aykroyd, Harold Ramis, Sigourney Weaver
Metrocolor   105 min

Betelgeuse (Michael Keaton) is enamoured by an unlucky magician's assistant in the "afterlife waiting room"

BEETLEJUICE (1988)

This is visually a stunner and gives a whole new look at the afterlife. In concept it owes more than a passing nod to the successful *Topper* series of yesteryear. Well, the newly dead couple Adam Maitland (Alec Baldwin) and his wife Barbara (Geena Davis) are confined to a specific time zone and do have the ability under duress to make an impression on the world of dodgy presidents and Viagra-energised joss sticks. Unfortunately they get involved with this really OTT character called Betelgeuse played by that wonderful actor Michael Keaton. He gives a bravura performance that even out-braves Jack Nicholson's more pyrotechnic performances.

The newly demised couple are appalled by what the new owners of their recently quitted love nest are doing to it and want to get access to the sort of spookiness that makes becurlered blue rinses in thick cotton nighties run out into the night ululating at a high decibel setting. But of course there are procedures to be followed and the newly resident Deetzs don't own a nightie between them. It's all outrageously good fun and if it doesn't come over as exactly an advertisement for the afterlife it does promise that you won't be bored down the centuries to come.

Producer: Michael Bender for Warner Bros/Geffen
Director: Tim Burton
Writer: Michael McDowell, Warren Skaaren
DoP: Thomas Ackerman
Sfx: Chuck Gaspar, Robert Short
Cast: Alec Baldwin, Geena Davis, Michael Keaton
Technicolor   92 min.

HIGH SPIRITS (1988)

A vehicle for Peter O'Toole to go over the top and not seem out of place. O'Toole has a run-down castle that he has turned into a hotel – Castle Plunkett. He comes up with the startling idea that the answer to all his fiscal problems is ghosts. And American tourists. So he advertises for and gets a bus full of American tourists. And he lays on some ghosts. Predictably the quasi-ghosts get it all wrong and it is up to the resident real ghosts to put out for the penniless peer and give the tourists what they want. In the case of Steve Guttenberg this is Daryl Hannah. A six-foot vision of loveliness that is pursued for eternity through the castle by her jealous lover – until Guttenberg gets in the way and breaks the chain. Daryl gets it together with Guttenberg and the lover, Liam Neeson, makes Steve's wife, Beverly D'Angelo, extremely happy. Meanwhile O'Toole has done a deal with head ghost, Ray McAnally, and the Castle Hotel is saved.

Producer: Stephen Woolley, David Saunders for
   Palace/Vision PDG
Director: Neil Jordan
Writer: Neil Jordan
DoP: Alex Thomson
Cast: Peter O'Toole, Daryl Hannah, Steve Guttenberg,
   Beverly D'Angelo, Liam Neeson, Ray McAnally
Colour   97 mins.

ALWAYS (1989)

Pete (Richard Dreyfuss) has to face the facts: his wife Dorinda (Holly Hunter) in the arms of another man (Brad Johnson)

(Remake of *A Guy Named Joe*, 1944)

I liked *Always*. But then anything with an aeroplane as the lead player gets my vote. It has a lot of excitement, fire, flying, hostility and Holly Hunter in a sweat-stained singlet. Unfortunately it also has Richard Dreyfus in a role for which he is totally unsuited.

Storyline goes: Dreyfuss and Hunter are an item. Hunter wants to give up flying and, with Dreyfus, take jobs as air traffic controller and flying instructor respectively. Dreyfus isn't too happy about giving up his macho job of putting out fires from the air but agrees. Then he takes on one mission too far and, in an act of heroism, succumbs. The act of heroism was to quench the fire aboard his pal Al's plane by dumping on him. Unfortunately his plane also catches fire but Al doesn't reciprocate the favour. Instead he swans off and comforts Hunter now that dreary Dreyfus is no longer with us. But unfortunately he is – in the non-shape of a ghost. It all comes down to a lot of agonising by Dreyfus as he watches Hunter in the arms of Al and a last scene where he can either let her die and join him in the afterlife or save her and watch her walk off into the sunset with Al. He saves her.

Producer: Steven Spielberg, Frank Marshall, Kathleen Kennedy for UIP/Amblin
Director: Steven Spielberg
Writer: Jerry Belson, Diane Thomas
DoP: Michael Salomon
Cast: Richard Dreyfuss, Holly Hunter, Brad Johnson
DeLuxe 123 min.

GHOST DAD (1990)

If ghosts are lightweight, this goes into negative balance. A pick-up on Bill Cosby's long running TV show that didn't work. That doesn't include Cosby: he worked his little cotton socks off but the opposition could sink an iceberg. Opposition being the kids this definitely tedious film is supposed to be all about.

Cosby is killed in an accident. As a dad he just about made it biologically but, in spite of yearnings to be Dad of the Year, he never made it psychologically. Which means that all his kids, three of 'em, are emotionally traumatised. Cosby, for no good reason, is given time off by God or Peter or someone, to show what an excellent father he would have made if he had given himself a chance. Believe me, with those kids he was better off in the afterworld – either up or down.

In the truest of Hollywood gluiest endings everything is resolved drippingly and Dad drifts off to his eternal rest – thank God.

Producer: Terry Nelson for Universal/SAH
Director: Sidney Poitier
Writer: Chris Reese
DoP: Andrew Laszlo
Cast: Bill Cosby, Ian Bannen
DeLuxe 84 min.

*Ray (Kevin Costner) with his daughter
Karen (Gaby Hoffman) on his shoulders*

FIELD OF DREAMS (1989)

Sports films are always a hard sell. Motor Racing is a good example. In spite of the glamour and danger, the luxurious international setting and the abundant opportunities for outrageous storylines there has never been a really successful movie based on the track. Maybe because sport itself is a kind of drama based on its own set of rules – dramas about dramas always seem at last two steps removed from reality.

So what chance has baseball?

Exactly! So why then is this film so good? Answer – it is actually about a man's natural desire to do

something unnatural. Iowa farmer Ray Kinsella is not one of your natural sons of the earth. Ploughing the fields and scattering manure might be alright as a mind-numbing chore but what really matters to Ray is baseball. His passion settles on a long dead baseball hero, Shoeless Joe Jackson. Then, between sowing the corn and worming the cows, Ray gets the call from the standing cereal that if he builds a baseball stadium Shoeless Joe will appear. Not only that – he will bring a whole cavalcade of sporting heroes with him.

Understandably Ray's neighbours think he is nuts. On the verge of bankruptcy, he is drawn to an old sports writer in Boston. He doesn't seem to say much but Ray's interpretation of what he does say gives him the inspiration and fortitude to endure the jibes and sniggers of ignorant neighbours and switch on the floodlights. From the corn, which is higher than a baseball player's beanie, steps shoeless Joe Jackson – followed by all the other legendary players who have just been sitting it out in purgatory for one last squat in the dug-out. Ray is vindicated, wife is reconciled and dumb kid is proud. And the neighbours? They are fit to be knocked down with an ethereal baseball bat.

Producer: Lawrence Gordon, Charlie Gordon for
  Guild/Universal/Carolco
Director: Phil Alden Robinson
Writer: Phil Alden Robinson
DoP: John Lindley
Music: James Horner.
Cast: Kevin Costner
DeLuxe   106 min.

HAUNTED (1995)

Heavyweight director Lewis Gilbert was brought in to try and make the ghost film respectable. He got together a good main cast and, to put the cherry on the plumcake, levered John Gielgud into a cameo role. It's very much in the genre. A pity really because with the array of stars and a director who knows which way to point the camera, it should have written a new chapter in ghost films. If it does I missed the point. It is beautifully acted and tells a simple story about a woman who feels she is being unfairly victimised by spirits from beyond the veil. She calls in a psychic investigator, a latterday Harry Price. For him the effects go off on cue and frequently. Prepare to be amazed as you sit in the dark and marvel at what's going on. But don't think. It could so easily have been a classic in the lens

of a different cameraman who could have made something dark murky and mysterious of the story. Unfortunately he wanterd every frame to be seen in the minutest detail and where half seen images would have told the story and titillated the fright buds, daylight kept the frighteners away. Special mention in dispatched for Quinn. His baby blue eyes registered astonishment before the astonishing began.

Producer: Anthony Andrews, Lewis Gilbert for
  Entertainment
Director: Lewis Gilbert
Writer: Tim Prager, Lewis Gilbert
(Based on a novel by James Herbert)
Cast: Aidan Quinn, Kate Beckinsale, Anthony
  Andrews, John Gielgud, Anna Massey
Colour   110 min.

GHOST (1990)

Come on! With the cast this film got who needs a story? The three leads fit their roles more closely than a Lycra tracksuit. Even fourth-placed man and villain of the piece is exactly right for his comeuppance.

It all starts on a downtown street that only a lobotomized moron with a death wish would walk along without a National Guard escort. This doesn't seem to occur to our hero and heroine. Perhaps that's what you had to do to be heroic those days. Anyway, out of nowhere a thug appears and puts paid to Sam's future as a budding security executive when he sticks a knife in upwardly mobile Sam's shirt front and leaves him to expire in Molly's arms. Only Sam doesn't know he is expired and it comes as a bit of a shock when he gets back to the place of his demise and finds Molly flooding him with tears in a widening pool of blood.

Sam has the qualifications for a term of haunting so elects to look after Molly. It isn't long before he learns that his old buddy Carl is the author of his misfortune. But how does he convey his newly won knowledge to Molly? Through Whoopi Goldberg, of course. Whoopi plays Old Mae, a cranky would-be medium who gets more than she bargained for when Sam decides to use her to get through to Molly.

All ends well with the evil Carl being dragged off by black-clad demons from hell while Sam floats off to a much more commodious place. But not before he has had a little extra-spiritual dalliance with Molly – using Old Mae's body would you believe. Whatever next!

Producer: Lisa Weinstein for UIP/Paramount/Howard W. Koch
Director: Jerry Zucker
Writer: Bruce Joel Rubin
DoP: Adam Greenberg
Cast: Patrick Swayze, Demi Moore, Whoopi Goldberg, Tony Goldwyn
Technicolor   127 min.

HAMLET (1991)

If you have Mel Gibson and Glenn Close surrounded by Alan Bates, Paul Scofield, Ian Holm and Helena Bonham-Carter in a film that is claimed to be British (European really) and penned by the greatest script writer of them all, what do you say to a gorilla who takes a seat in the row in front of you and insists on throwing his banana skins in your lap? Hamlet (Mel Gibson) has been done so many times that drunks on their third bottle of vintage meths and rolling in a gutter in Wardour Street can be heard to mutter the indecisive line "To be. Or not to be!" It's every actor's dream and every schoolboy's nightmare. In between there is Laurence Olivier who cannot be denied. So the arcane hero of Shakespearean rewrites, Franco Zefferelli, decided that Olivier had wrung everything out of the role, as is, and added a new dimension – Mel Gibson. It was just what it needed to bring it into a world pigged out on mumbling anti-heroes and buckets of popcorn. The purists may sneer but all I can say is – didn't he do well?

One of the great innovations, as far as this book is concerned, is that he brought The Ghost of Hamlet's Father (Paul Scofield) out of the flies and under the lights. And you don't give a thespian of Scofield's ilk a chance like that and expect an ethereal shade. Would Big Bill approve? He might think the shift in emphasis away from the usual moody Dane and the focus on Gertrude (Glenn Close), claiming a star vehicle, is a little outside the parameters, but there's still enough blood and guts to send him back to Stratford with a jingle in his pocket and a broad smile. And then there is truculent but decidedly dishy Ophelia (Helena Bonham-Carter).

Producer: Dyson Lovell for Warner/Nelson Entertainment/Icon
Director: Franco Zeffirelli
Writer: Christopher DeVore
DoP: David Watkin
Music: Ennio Morricone
Art Director: Michael Lamont
Cast: Mel Gibson, Glenn Close, Alan Bates, Paul Scofield, Ian Holm, Helena Bonham-Carter
Colour   135 min.

TRULY, MADLY, DEEPLY (1990)

This is a wonderful film with everything to recommend it. Some critics have been less then generous with Anthony Minghella's directing, claiming that his long association with TV has somehow inhibited what he puts on the screen. This point of view is, of course, worthy of consideration before bringing in the verdict of – rubbish! The nature of the film demands a still, closed-in atmosphere as an arena for the actors to put in very delicate performances. How else would you portray a love story where the heroine Nina (Juliet Stevenson), grief stricken and inconsolable following the death of her lover Jamie (Alan Rickman), comes home to find him playing the cello in the front parlour.

And that's not the end of it. Before long he's bringing ghostly mates home and generally deadening up the place. The underlying question is whether Nina will decide that if the afterlife is so companionable what point is there in hanging around an empty flat fighting off the advances of blokes who think that she has been without it for long enough to give them a chance to work their magic.

Set in London, it manages to give off the aura that is all too well known to single women in the wicked city. There are plenty of places to go to, hundreds of galleries, exhibitions, shows, walks and just about anything you want to see but they are all meaningless without someone to share them with. The only male who comes out creditably in this film is Sandy, the boss of the agency where Nina works. He plays a gritty, down to earth Scot-with-a-heart to perfection and gives a performance every bit as good as the leads. Titus (Christopher Rozycki) represents the serpent in the Garden of Eden – or a flat in Maida Vale. His only interest is getting into the grieving Nina's knickers and insidiously installs himself in her flat on the pretext of giving it a makeover.

The only part of the film that I didn't unconditionally love was the ending. A little too predictable I thought. But there you go. I can't think of a better one so I'll have to go along with it as it is.

Producer: Robert Cooper for Samuel Goldwyn
  Company/Winston/BBC/Lionheart
Director: Anthony Minghella
Writer: Anthony Minghella
DoP: Remi Adefarasin
Music: Barrington Pheloung
Cast: Juliet Stevenson, Alan Rickman, Bill Paterson
Colour   106 min.

CITY OF ANGELS (1998)

Nicolas Cage is not one of my favourite actors. He never seems to do anything ordinary – like wash and shave. And send his clothes to the cleaners? Forget it. So he's not exactly my ideal casting for an angel. Whereas Meg Ryan is.

City of Angels is a nice, compact story along familiar lines. Angel of Death meets doctor, falls in love, gives up the death job, loses girl. That's the story line. The way it gets from point A, the death and collection by angel Nicolas of a little girl spirit to the Z of ex-angel Nicolas, bound by an earthly existence and mouthing the modern equivalent of "It's better to have loved and lost, than never to have shared a tube of toothpaste!" that makes this film so watchable.

The set-piece of the black Armani-clad, Ray-Ban-bespectacled angels lining up on the sea front at Venice Beach to stare at the rising sun is a tableau that sticks in the mind. And libraries will never be the same again. That's where Death's messengers while away the time when they're not slaving over a hot deathbed. I'm not sure why they use the library as the equivalent of a biker's caff. Perhaps it's all those dead authors whom they probably know personally.

Nick and Meg make it through Nick's unselfish act of casting off immortality. Such a sacrilegious act has to have a price. And the price is a six-hanky final reel.

It's a film I shall see again. Just to make sure there weren't any bits in there I may have missed. Like why, after having been grabbing souls for eternity, Nick gets sexually involved with a potential inductee. Or is there some obscure line in the script that explains the Armani costumes? Or is that just a triumph of business acumen over artistic preference by the wardrobe department? Or, if Nick Cage is immortal and can wing around freely without even asking Scottie to beam him up, how can he kill himself by falling off a skyscraper?

But is it a ghost story? Don't let my hang-ups spoil it for you. It's one of the best films I've seen for quite a while.

Producers: Dawn Steel and Charles Roven
Director: Brad Silberling
DoP: John Seale
Writer: Dana Stevens
(based on the film *Wings of Desire*)
Cast: Nicolas Cage, Meg Ryan, Dennis Franz, André
  Braugher